Louis Pasteur
Fighting Hero of Science
(1822–1895)

Also by Madeleine Grant

Wonder World of Microbes
Microbiology and Human Progress
Biology and World Health

LOUIS PASTEUR
Fighting Hero of Science

by *MADELEINE P. GRANT*

PROFESSOR OF BIOLOGY AND BACTERIOLOGY
SARAH LAWRENCE COLLEGE

illustrated with photographs,

and with line drawings by CLIFFORD GEARY

Whittlesey House

McGRAW-HILL BOOK COMPANY, INC.

New York   Toronto   London

JB
P

I am indebted to the Librairie Ernest Flammarion, Paris, for permission to quote from *Correspondance de Pasteur*. My deepest
gratitude goes to Dr. René Dubos of The Rockefeller Institute in
New York, a distinguished bacteriologist and author of *Louis
Pasteur: Free Lance of Science*. Dr. Dubos extended many
favors to me while I was writing this book, and generously took
time from his very crowded schedule to read the manuscript in
galley proof. It is a pleasure to express here my appreciation of
his assistance.

3-18-60

To ALZADA COMSTOCK
in appreciation of her wit and wisdom, and
with gratitude for the role she played in my
flight to France during the writing of this book

Foreword

FLYING ACROSS the Atlantic in a plane bound for Paris, I knew that in a few hours I would stand before the Sorbonne where Louis Pasteur had studied, walk in the Luxembourg Gardens and see the Palace as he had seen it, visit the Pasteur Institute which he had founded, and go to Villeneuve l'Etang where he died. Then I would travel south and walk around the tanning pits in the basement of his birthplace at Dôle, and see the village of Arbois in the foothills of the Jura mountains where he lived as a young boy. As a student of science and teacher of biology, I had for many years looked upon Pasteur as a great scientific hero. It was exciting to feel that now I would come to know him as a very real human being.

So many French people greeted me with friendliness and expressed such veneration for Pasteur that my own admiration and affection for him increased. I shall never forget the devotion to Louis Pasteur expressed by Mlle. Denise Wrotnowska, Curator of the Museum at the Pasteur Institute, as she went with me from room to room in his spacious apartment discussing many items of interest; nor the rare opportunity of meeting Professor Pasteur Vallery-Radot in his medical office and talking with him about more personal matters concerning his grandfather. The four-volume *Correspondance de Pasteur* collected

and annotated by his grandson will live as an affectionate
memorial.

Mme. Mazoué of the *Association des Françaises—
Diplomées des Universitées* made it possible for me to see
the work now in progress in the polio and rabies laboratories of the Pasteur Institute. It was here with her and
with Mme. Bushnell, a professional biologist of the *Lab-
oratorie de Physiologie Acoustique* in Jouy-en-Josas, that
I sensed the continuation of the ideals of scientific research established seventy years ago by its first director.

The excitement of my adventure increased when Mlle.
Jacqueline de Susbielle, a university student studying to
be an interpreter, started off with me in a little French
car to drive south to Dôle and Arbois. Monsieur Auguste
Ventard, Curator of *La Maison Natale* at Dôle, gave generously of his time showing us through the rooms of the
little tannery, which thousands visit annually. The next
day he drove with us to Arbois, and continued to talk
about Pasteur with such deep feeling that it was easy to
appreciate the humble origin of this great Frenchman.

I hope that many who read this book may wish to go to
France and "meet" Louis Pasteur as I did.

M.P.G.

Contents

CHAPTER 1

Vaccination: A Medical Revolution

IT WAS JULY 6, 1885, when Louis Pasteur, looking up from his microscope, saw nine-year-old Joseph Meister come limping into his laboratory in Paris. Joseph was with his mother and a neighbor, Monsieur Vone. The three had left their little French village near the Swiss border and started for the city of Paris in search of the one man who might save the life of young Joseph.

Pasteur loved children, and the heart of this great scientist filled with horror when he learned that two days previously Joseph had been furiously attacked by a mad dog. The boy's hands, arms, and legs were badly bitten. The cuts in one arm were very deep. All in all, there were fourteen ugly wounds.

It had happened at eight o'clock in the morning when Joseph was on his way to school in the village of Meissengott in Alsace. The dog jumped on him and threw him to the ground. A nearby bricklayer ran to his rescue, and with an iron bar beat off the dog, which ran home only to bite even its master, M. Vone, who grabbed a gun and shot it dead.

When the bricklayer picked Joseph up, he found him bleeding and covered with saliva from the dog. Examination of the contents of the dead dog's stomach showed that it was filled with hay, straw, and sticks of wood. The dog had been biting anything and everything it met as it madly tore about. There was no doubt about it, this angry dog had *rabies*—a deadly disease found among wild animals, especially wolves. Animals with this disease are called *rabid,* and the dog that attacked Joseph had sometime previously been bitten by a rabid animal.

For centuries the people of Alsace had lived in dread of mad wolves that strayed down from the Jura mountains and attacked dogs and human beings, spreading the disease among their victims. To be bitten by a rabid animal was almost always fatal. Joseph's parents were terrified. It did not seem possible that their son could live.

That evening, twelve hours after the accident, they had taken him to a country doctor, Dr. Weber, who burned Joseph's wounds with carbolic acid. He urged them to take him at once to Paris—a two-day journey. There they must find and consult Louis Pasteur who, although not a physician, would know more than anyone else whether there was any chance of saving their son.

"Pasteur has saved dogs from rabies," said Dr. Weber. "Perhaps he can save Joseph." Joseph and his mother, accompanied by M. Vone, started at once on the long journey.

Pasteur was deeply moved at the sight of these three strangers: the frightened and suffering young boy, his grief-stricken mother, and the anxious and bewildered M. Vone. He carefully examined the man and soon assured him that he need have no concern about himself, for his coat sleeve had been heavy enough to protect his skin against the dog's teeth when it had grabbed his arm. Since his skin showed not even the slightest scratch, the rabies virus in the dog's saliva could not possibly have entered his system. Pasteur assured him that he could safely return home. Relieved but with a heavy heart, he went back to Meissengott, knowing that Joseph's life hung in the balance.

Pasteur turned to examine the young boy. The kindly face of this great scientist was sad and grave, for he knew that he must quickly make a serious and most difficult decision. What should he do for this boy? Did he dare to risk using the preventive rabies vaccine that he had successfully used on dogs? He had never tried his treatment on a human being. But he was sure of his experiments with dogs, because he had repeated them many times during the past four years.

First he had vaccinated healthy dogs against rabies by using material from the spinal cord of rabbits that had been injected with the rabies virus. The treatment consisted in giving dogs a series of twelve or more daily injections of emulsions of dried spinal cords of rabid rabbits. Such cords, dried for fourteen days, were so changed that emulsions of them were harmless, and yet they possessed the ability to stimulate the body of healthy dogs to make protective substances against the deadly virus. A cord dried thirteen days contained slightly stronger yet still harmless material. Daily injections of cords which had been dried for shorter and shorter periods were given until the treated animal actually resisted a final injection of the deadly virus itself. In fact, dogs treated in this way did not succumb to the disease even when bitten by a rabid dog. Pasteur knew that he could vaccinate dogs and protect them against rabies.

Even more important, he had recently saved the lives of dogs *after* they had been bitten, by giving them the same treatment. In all his experiments he had used over one hundred dogs, and he was very sure of his results. But he was not a physician and therefore had no legal right to treat a human being. Then, too, no one could be absolutely sure how the human body would respond to these injections. He must first consult Professor Vulpian, a physiologist, and Dr. Grancher, a physician, who were both scientists familiar with his work. He hurried off to see them, for there was no time to waste.

The experts whom Pasteur consulted were of one opinion: Joseph *must* be given the Pasteur treatment against rabies. There was no other choice. If only the boy had been taken at once to a blacksmith's shop and had had his wounds cauterized by a red-hot iron, he might have had some slight chance of recovering. But there were fourteen wounds, some very deep, and they had been treated with carbolic acid twelve hours after the accident. The skin was broken in too many places, and the carbolic treatment had been used too late to give protection. His case was considered hopeless unless something drastic could be done. Pasteur's vaccine had saved

the life of dogs. It might save the life of Joseph Meister.
The first of the long series of daily injections was begun
that night, almost sixty hours after the accident.

It was agreed, for two reasons, that Dr. Grancher
should give the injections. First, Pasteur's left hand was
paralyzed from a stroke suffered when he was only forty-
six years old, and it would have been difficult for him
to handle the Pravaz syringe. Most important of all,
however, he was not a physician and had no wish to treat
Joseph illegally.

Pasteur arranged for the lodgings of Joseph and his
mother at Rollin Collège, in Paris, and anxiously watched
over the boy day and night. With great care, he directed
the preparation of each dose. He was always present
when the injections were given, making detailed notes of
every step in the treatment.

As the days passed, Joseph's wounds grew less painful,
and he learned not to dread the puncture of the needle
when it was placed just under the skin of the abdomen.
Joseph soon became very fond of the elderly man who
took such an interest in him, who was so kind and gentle,
and who even let him play with the guinea pigs in the
laboratory cages.

But as the treatment continued, Pasteur was tormented
with the fear that the boy might not survive in spite of
his seeming good health, because the scientist knew only
too well that the symptoms of rabies sometimes suddenly
appear many weeks after the victim is bitten. On July
11, five days after the first injection, Pasteur wrote to his
son-in-law:

All is going well, the child sleeps well, has a good appetite, and the inoculated matter is absorbed into the system from one day to another without leaving a trace. It is true that I have not yet come to the test inoculations, which will take place Tuesday, Wednesday and Thursday. If the lad keeps well during the following weeks, I think the experiment will be sure to succeed.

Each inoculation was stronger than the previous one, and as the end of the treatment approached, Pasteur's anxiety increased. Mme. Pasteur wrote to their children: "Your father has had another bad night; yet there can be no turning back now! The boy continues in perfect health."

The series of vaccinations lasted ten days, and Joseph received twelve shots. On July 16, at 11 A.M., he had his last injection. When Joseph went to bed that night, he threw his arms around "Dear Monsieur Pasteur," as he had come to call him. While Joseph slept soundly, Pasteur spent a wretched night dreaming that the boy might die from the final, most powerful injection. But Joseph lived!

Pasteur, exhausted from so many days of mental anguish, left Paris for a short rest in the quiet country estate of his son-in-law in Burgundy. Joseph remained in Paris for several days under the watchful care of Dr. Grancher, who kept Pasteur informed of the boy's health. But Pasteur could not calm down, and each morning anxiously waited reports from Paris. The news continued good.

By the end of July, Pasteur went as usual with Mme. Pasteur to spent the summer in his boyhood home in the town of Arbois. He refused to form hasty conclusions on the result of Joseph's treatment, but as the summer passed and Joseph remained well, his doubts vanished. By October, he was ready to report to the Academy of Sciences in Paris on his "Method of Preventing Rabies after a Bite." He announced:

After I might say innumerable experiments, I have arrived at a preventive method, practical and prompt, the success of which has been so convincing in dogs that I have confidence in its general application in all animals and even in man.

After describing the details of the treatment of Joseph Meister, Pasteur concluded: "Today, three months and three weeks after the accident, his health leaves nothing to be desired." He went on to tell of the second lad who had just come to him for treatment.

On October 14, six young peasant boys were watching their sheep in a meadow at the foot of the Jura mountains when suddenly they spied a large dog. Its jaw was hanging open and the animal was frothing at the mouth. "A mad dog!" they cried out. Seeing the children, the dog dashed across the meadow, and the children ran shrieking in all directions. The oldest, Jean Jupille, armed with a whip, fought the infuriated animal in order to protect the escape of the younger shepherds. The dog seized his left hand between its jaws. Jean wrestled with it, threw it to the ground, and tried to free his hand. While doing so, the dog savagely bit his right hand. Finally, Jean wound the whip around the dog's jaws, grabbed his wooden shoe, and beat the animal over the head. To make sure it was dead, he dragged it to a nearby stream and held its head under water. With both hands bleeding, Jean returned to the village.

His wounds were bandaged, and the dog's body was

recovered. The next day two veterinary surgeons declared that without doubt the dog had been rabid. The mayor of the village wrote to Pasteur giving him the whole story. Unless Jean Jupille could be vaccinated, the brave shepherd would die as a result of his own courage. Surely Pasteur could save him.

Pasteur answered immediately. He said that he had saved dogs bitten by a rabid dog if treatment was begun as late as six or even eight days after the biting. There was no time to waste, but Jean's parents must first consent to the treatment.

Jean started at once for Paris, but by the time he arrived, six days had passed since the accident. The interval in the case of Joseph Meister had been only two and one-half days. Had too much time been lost to save young Jupille?

Pasteur had reason to be worried, for he was not certain he could save Jean's life. Yet his success with little Joseph gave him courage. He started Jean at once on his series of daily injections, but was constantly worried for fear something might go wrong. The boy's health remained good, the lapse of six days had not been too long. The boy's life was saved. The injections had had time to stimulate the body to produce protective substances which destroyed the viruses before they could reach the brain. Once they were in the brain, no known treatment could have saved him.

In 1885 people were skeptical about new medical discoveries—doctors more than patients. So it was inevitable that some day a person would go to Pasteur after a lapse of more than six days from the time of being bitten.

Within a few weeks, Pasteur had to face just such a problem when Louise Pelletier was brought to him.

When he saw this little ten-year-old girl, he was filled with terror, for she had been severely bitten in the head thirty-three days earlier. The ugly wound was still an open sore. "This is a hopeless case," he thought to himself. "Rabies will no doubt appear at any moment. Whatever shall I do? If I treat her and she dies, people will say my method has failed. As a result, many bitten persons, discouraged from coming to the laboratory, will die of the disease. Shall I protect my method or fight a losing battle to save this little girl?" As these thoughts rushed through his mind, his compassion for the child and her parents, who begged him to try to save her, left him no choice.

Louise Pelletier completed the vaccine treatment and returned to school, but soon word came that she was dying. Pasteur rushed to her bedside, hoping that additional injections might yet save her. But it soon became evident that she would not live. She begged him not to leave her, nor could Pasteur bear to tear himself away. When all hope was gone, Pasteur turned to the parents and said, "I did so wish I could have saved your little one." As he left the house, he burst into tears.

As the months passed, news of the Pasteur treatment gradually spread far and wide, and hundreds of persons bitten by rabid dogs went to Paris for help. Nineteen Russians, one of them a priest who had been attacked by a wild wolf, reached Pasteur in serious condition. Sixteen of them survived.

As the number of persons receiving the rabies treatment increased, so naturally, for one reason or another, did the failures. During the year following the treatment of Joseph Meister, 1,726 French persons bitten by mad dogs were vaccinated, and all but ten of them lived. Some physicians, unable to accept such a revolutionary idea as treatment with a vaccine prepared by a mere chemist, made the most of every failure: they accused Pasteur of murder, claiming his treatment had caused the death of Louise Pelletier.

His friend and supporter, Dr. Grancher, described the rising feeling of hostility: "One day, I was at the Medical School for an examination ... I heard a furious voice shouting, 'Yes, Pasteur is an assassin!' I walked in and saw a group of colleagues, who dispersed in silence."

At another time when supporting Pasteur against false accusations, Dr. Grancher said: "The medical men who have been chosen by M. Pasteur to assist him in his work have not hesitated to practise the anti-rabic inoculation on themselves, as a safeguard against an accidental inoculation of the virus which they are constantly handling. What greater proof can they give of their bona fide convictions?"

Although Pasteur knew that most medical men in Paris supported him, he was saddened by the bitterness of many angry debates. He received unsigned letters filled with false accusations. Insulting newspaper articles came off the presses, and mournfully he exclaimed, "I did not know I had so many enemies."

Some of his opponents were those who found it impossible to accept such a revolutionary idea as injecting into the human body the deadly rabies virus—no matter how weakened it might be. Even some of his own disciples wondered if enough work had been done on dogs to warrant its use in man. Some people even opposed experimenting with animals. Probably some of his enemies were those who still fought against the idea that microbes could cause disease, even though Pasteur had given convincing evidence to support this theory. And there were those who, always on the alert for slander, joined the forces of the opposition and gave support to smear campaigns.

Whenever Pasteur's adversaries attacked his work because of prejudice, without scientific evidence to support their criticisms, he lost his temper, his gentleness vanished, and in an aggressive manner he fought for the truth as he saw it. In this way he often antagonized others by the mere force and brilliance of his intellectual vigor. He had an unwavering confidence in himself whenever he was forced to fight ignorance, superstition, or prejudice.

To his great satisfaction and peace of mind, a commission of experts was appointed by the British government to repeat his work. Its members confirmed his experiments on dogs, and went to Paris to examine his clinical records of human cases. They even made detailed inquiries in the homes of ninety patients who had received the anti-rabies treatment. They finally concluded:

From the evidence of all these facts, we think it certain that the inoculations practised by M. Pasteur on persons bitten by rabid animals have prevented the occurrence of hydrophobia [rabies]

in a large proportion of those who, if they had not been so inoculated, would have died of that disease.

Even more important than Pasteur's contribution to
the control of rabies was the fact that he established the
idea that men, women, and little children could be protected against various diseases by vaccination—by injections of the weakened or dead microbe that caused the
disease.

Over one hundred years before the days of Pasteur,
Jenner had vaccinated people in England against smallpox. But Jenner had not *made* his vaccine. He had
protected people against smallpox by injecting the fluid
from sores on the hands of milkmaids afflicted with cowpox. Furthermore, Jenner had no theory to explain how
his vaccine worked, and therefore the practice could not
be applied to other diseases. Pasteur supported his own
practice by well-founded theories, and was the first to
discover that vaccines can be *made*. It was Pasteur who
prepared the way for other men to make vaccines for
other diseases.

Pasteur lived for ten years after saving the life of Joseph
Meister, long enough to see erected in Paris the great
Pasteur Institute which has served as a clinic for rabies
treatment and as a research center for the study of other
diseases caused by microbes. He rejoiced in knowing
that the money which made this building possible came
pouring in from French citizens, rich and poor alike:
from contributions from his own government, from the
Czar of Russia, and Emperor Pedro II of Brazil. His pride
rose when he read the name of Joseph Meister among the

long list of individual donors who had contributed whatever they could.

If he were living today, he would know that over sixty Pasteur Institutes have now been built in many quarters of the world. At the Institute in Paris numerous enlargements have been made, the most modern equipment has been added, and people go there to be vaccinated not only against rabies but also against yellow fever and tuberculosis.

The most recent development from Pasteur's work is the Salk vaccine against polio. Few people realize that it was the pioneer work of Pasteur on rabies that laid the foundation for vaccination against polio. Today, in an annex of the Pasteur Institute in Paris, a French modification of the Salk vaccine is made, and thousands of children in France are being protected against polio.

Pasteur was a chemist trained to work with nonliving things. What led him to study living germs? What gave him the idea that vaccines could be made? Was it an accident or the result of carefully planned experiments? Why did he select rabies as the first disease for human vaccination? Why is he called a great benefactor of all mankind?

It is never easy to explain how some people achieve greatness, but the early years in a person's life are often the most important. Some of the reasons which explain how Pasteur became a fighting hero of science may be discovered in learning about his parents, his life at home, his teachers, and his friends.

CHAPTER 2

The Early Years

LOUIS PASTEUR's ancestors were humble French peasants.
For centuries they had lived in Franche-Comté, a region
in France near the Jura mountains bordering on Switzer-
land. Some of them had been serfs who could not legally
leave the estate of their lord and master. They tilled the
soil, harvested and milled the grain, and labored in the
vineyards of some nobleman who looked upon them as
part of his possessions. The French word *pasteur* means
"shepherd." Some of Pasteur's ancestors watched sheep
and oxen graze in the wide-open meadows at the foothills of these mountains. They were intelligent, hard-
working, simple people.

Louis' great grandfather, Claude Pasteur, who was
born a serf, longed to be a free man. By the time he was
thirty years old, he had saved enough money to buy his
independence. The deed that freed him stated that
Claude Pasteur and all his descendants from that time
forth should be free from the stigma of serfdom. Claude
then worked in a tannery, where he learned to make
leather from animal skins, and was so successful that later
he came to have a tannery of his own.

Louis' father was Jean-Joseph Pasteur. He had been left an orphan when very young and his aunts had brought him up. Although they gave him kindness, he received only a meager education. They thought it more important that he learn the trade of his father and grandfather and therefore put him to work in a tannery. In 1811, when he was just twenty years old, he was drafted into the army of Napoleon I, and sent to join a regiment invading Spain.

Over two-thirds of these soldiers never lived to see France again. Jean-Joseph, however, lived through the fierce fighting, and with the few surviving comrades, he returned to France in 1815. For his bravery in battle he was promoted to the rank of Sergeant Major and presented the Cross of the Legion of Honor from the hands of the Emperor himself.

After the downfall of Napoleon in 1815, Jean-Joseph received his discharge from the army at the age of twenty-four. Like many others who had risen from the people, he idolized Napoleon. He had fought for the ideals of the Revolution—for fraternity, equality, and liberty. Now grief-stricken, he saw his beloved country vanquished and humiliated. He longed for the rehabilitation of France and the restoration of the Republic, but there was nothing for him to do but return to the little village of Salins and to the monotonous job in a tannery.

Within a short time he made the acquaintance of a family of market gardeners named Roqui, who lived on the other side of the river, just across from the tannery. Most every morning at early dawn, Jean-Joseph watched

Jeanne Roqui busily working in the garden, and it was soon obvious that his interest in her was more than a neighborly one.

The Roquis, like the Pasteurs, could trace their ancestry back 200 years. Theirs was one of the most ancient plebian families in Franche-Comté. Jeanne was a kind, modest, and intelligent peasant girl. Jean-Joseph, a serious, melancholy man, loved her gaiety and enthusiasm. The difference in their natures seemed to increase their affection for each other, and in 1816 Jean-Joseph Pasteur and Jeanne Roqui were married in the Catholic church of St. Jean-Baptiste in Salins.

The young couple migrated about 20 miles north to the ancient city of Dôle, which had been the capital of Franche-Comté. Here they settled in a very modest house on the Street of Tanners, which ran along the edge of a canal from the Doubs River. Tanners always lived close to the bank of a river, for in making leather it was necessary to wash the skins in running water.

Their first child, a boy, lived only a few months. In 1818 they had a little girl named Virginie, and four years later, on December 27, 1822, a baby boy was born. They named him Louis. In the Catholic church in Dôle, he was later baptized "Louis, son of Jean-Joseph Pasteur Monsieur and Jeanne-Etiennette Roqui, his wife." As the weeks passed, there was great rejoicing, because this baby boy was strong and healthy.

The little front room in which Louis was born was just above the cellar where animal skins soaked in deep pits of tannic acid. Little Virginie, who was four years old,

could just peek over his crib and call him "Louis." Her
mother had always been busy baking, sewing, and mend-
ing, but now she seemed busier than ever. Virginie
wished that Louis did not sleep so much.

Jean-Joseph, proud to have a son, worked day after day
in the tannery. He received fresh skins of sheep and cattle shipped down the river. First the skins were covered
with salt and stored in salt bins. Then after scraping off
all the fur, he soaked them in deep tanning pits. Using
long iron tongs, he put in first a layer of skins, then a layer
of chips of fresh oak bark, then a layer of skins, and so
on until the pit was full. Next he carried two large
wooden buckets to the edge of the river and filled them
with water to pour into the pit. It took many a bucket-
ful, for the pits were five feet wide and ten feet deep. The
water dissolved the tannin in the bark, making a solution of tannic acid. The skins soaked for a whole year
and when they were brown and tanned, Jean-Joseph took
them out—again using the long iron tongs—and rinsed
them in the river. The dripping skins were then hung
up to air and dry. Jean-Joseph scraped off the loose,
outside, fleshy fibers, and hammered and pounded the
pelts to make them firm and strong.

From the cellar, Jean-Joseph carried large pieces of
brown pelt to the workshop upstairs just behind the room
where baby Louis slept. He spread them on a long
wooden table, and worked on them piece by piece. He
rubbed and scraped with a *marguerite,* a heavy, iron-
toothed tool which he pushed with his right hand. As he
rubbed, he sprinkled oil from a *guipon,* which he held

in his left hand. Moving first one arm then the other, in rhythmic motions, he toiled with all his strength until the leather was soft and pliable. It was rough, heavy, and dirty work. Jean-Joseph thought: "Little Louis must never be a tanner!"

Above the cellar there were two other rooms, a bedroom and, across the hall, a more spacious room which ran the width of the house. This latter was used as the family living room, dining room, kitchen, and "store." It was here that people came to buy leather for boots, harnesses, belts, gloves, and purses. Grandmother Roqui took charge of "the store," and Jeanne helped her husband keep the accounts. People liked the fine leather Jean-Joseph made.

There was great excitement one day when Louis was three years old. He and Virginie acquired a new baby sister, Josephine. The little home seemed very crowded now, and a year later, Jean-Joseph decided to move his family to a house in Marnoz which old grandmother Roqui had given them. He hoped the stream nearby would make it possible for him to establish a tannery.

So one day Jean-Joseph loaded the household furniture into an old farm wagon and carefully packed in all the tanning tools: the marguerites, the guipons, the long iron tongs, the wooden workbenches, the buckets, and the little oil lamps. Finally, when they were ready to start, Jean-Joseph took the reins of the horse and mounted to the driver's seat. Virginie helped Louis, who was four years old, into the long, low-slung wagon, and their mother, holding baby Josephine in her arms, took the seat beside her husband.

Off the little family started for Marnoz, 20 miles south of Dôle. This would be a long drive, and they would have to stop for lunch and give the horse time to rest. They drove past hillsides covered with apple orchards and vineyards, and finally, toward the end of the day, they arrived in Marnoz. Just in the distance, they could see Mt. Poupet, which rose like a large dome against the sky.

Soon Louis made friends with the little children of the village. One day when he was playing with them, a stranger appeared who was climbing the hilly road to Aiglepierre. The man stopped and offered a small coin to the one who could first reach the top of the nearest hill. Louis, who was not quite five, with jet-black hair and bright, gray-green eyes, stared eagerly at the stranger. In great excitement, all the children started off up the hill, and Louis ran as fast as his short legs could carry him, reaching the top far ahead of anyone else. He clutched his prize in his hot little hand. It looked so shiny and seemed so big! What would his parents say when he told them all about it? Louis never forgot winning this race, even though he could not recall the trip to Marnoz and all the excitement of his first journey.

The family's sojourn in Marnoz was brief, because the little stream that ran near the house was too small to establish a good business. Seven miles away, in Arbois, there was a good tannery for sale, and so once more they packed all their belongings. Louis now had another little baby sister, Emilie, and this time father, mother, and four children started off in an old wagon, bound for Arbois.

As the wooden wagon creaked over the muddy roads, they passed tall poplar trees, rich farm gardens, and neatly trimmed vineyards. As they reached the top of a mountain road, they looked down and saw the little town of Arbois nestled below, with its white cement houses and red roofs. The tall, square tower of the village church, Saint-Just, stood outlined against the sky.

They descended the hill and came to the bridge over the Cuisance River which marked the entrance to the town. No sooner had they crossed the bridge than Jean-Joseph pulled the reins tight and stopped in front of the first house on the right. This was their new home. Its modest front was built close to the road, and the large back yard with its tanning pits stretched out about one hundred feet to the edge of the river. From here the rapid current of the Cuisance passed under the bridge and broke into a noisy waterfall. Jean-Joseph hoped that this would be a good location for his business, and indeed it was, for the Pasteur family never moved again.

Odors of decaying skins mixed with the smells of the tanning process soon filled the yard. The Pasteur home was always open to Louis' friends, who often came to the tannery. They liked to play in the back yard with the chips of bark and bits of iron that were always about, but they thought the tannery smells were dreadful. Louis loved his home, his sisters, and his parents, and he was accustomed to tannery odors. They were just a part of what meant home to him.

Jean-Joseph was eager to give Louis the best possible education, and it was an exciting day for the whole family

when Louis started off, lunch box in hand, to go to his
first class in the primary school which was a section of
the Collège d'Arbois (a private high school). It was only
about a half mile away from home, so he could easily
walk.

Here Louis learned to read and spell by a method of
mutual teaching in which one pupil who had learned the
rudiments taught others to spell aloud in a sing-song
fashion. The teacher passed from group to group selecting *monitors* who became teachers of the others. In the
spring, when windows in the school were open, high,
shrill children's voices echoed through the courtyard. In
monotonous rhythms, some chanted the spelling of simple
words, while others in unison spelled out longer ones.

Louis loved each new lesson book that his father bought
him and proudly wrote his name on the first page. At
night Jean-Joseph helped him with his reading and encouraged him to keep his copybook neat and tidy. Louis
was a conscientious boy and always studied hard, but he
seemed to learn very slowly. He was the shortest pupil
in the primary school and eager to be the best. How he
longed to be chosen monitor, but he was only a mediocre
pupil.

When Louis was eight, he went into the grammar
grades at the Collège d'Arbois. Despite his own meager
education, Jean-Joseph continued to help Louis with his
lessons in geography, history, and arithmetic. He was
learning along with his son. Louis knew that Jean-
Joseph was often very tired after a hard day in the tannery, but he loved hearing his father tell about the great

Napoleon I and the past glories of France.   Jean-Joseph
taught Louis to love France and all things French.   Sometimes, however, Louis wished his father would smile now
and then and be gay like his mother.

Jean-Joseph was not one to go to a café and gossip with
others over a glass of wine.   He was a solitary man, deeply
absorbed in his own thoughts.   Although he never spoke
of his campaigns, every Sunday he dressed in a spotlessly
clean frock coat which he had decorated with the colorful ribbon of the Legion of Honor.   Louis went to Mass
every Sunday morning with his family, and in the afternoon Jean-Joseph took a solitary walk, passing his own
vineyards on the road to Besançon.   On these weekly
strolls he always thought about Louis.   "Just a mediocre
student," he would say to himself.   "Whatever will become of him?"   He was certain of only one thing—his
son must never be a tanner.

One day when Louis was still eight, three-year-old
Emilie became very ill.   They called it "brain fever."
She was sick for a long time, and although she continued
to grow, the fever permanently damaged her brain and
she remained mentally a little child.   Louis seemed to
have a special fondness for "poor Emilie," perhaps because she was so helpless.   Louis had gay times too.   In
the spring he loved to go trout fishing in the Cuisance
with his friend, Jules Vercel.   He envied Jules' skill in
casting a net, but he refused to go bird trapping because,
as he told his friends, he could not bear to see the suffering of an injured lark.

Sometimes during school holidays, Louis helped his father in the tannery, but never as an apprentice, because Jean-Joseph intended that nothing should ever interfere with Louis' education. His greatest hope was that some day, his son, even though just an ordinary student, might become a teacher.

When Louis was thirteen, he entered the secondary division of the Collège d'Arbois. This was the final and highest section of the school, corresponding to the American high school. It was here that the headmaster, M. Romanet, began to notice how carefully Louis worked. He saw that the boy never sat daydreaming at his desk, and that no noise ever distracted him. His copybook in geography, filled with the minutest details, was beautifully penned in a very fine, neat handwriting. As M. Romanet came to know him better, he understood that there was nothing slow about the way his mind worked. It was simply that the boy was never ready to speak unless he could be absolutely sure of what he said.

Although Louis liked his studies, he loved to draw portraits in pastels even more. The results were exquisite. One of his first paintings was of his mother, just as she looked as she started off to market. She wears a white bonnet neatly tied under her chin, and a blue-and-green plaid shawl over her shoulders. Her gay, kindly eyes lend a kind of serenity to an expression of strong determination. The drawing shows marked artistic ability and an honest attempt to paint every detail. This portrait and many others which he painted when a young boy have been saved, and experts who have studied them believe that Louis Pasteur might have become a great artist.

But people whom Louis loved and respected were influencing him in other directions. His father gave him no encouragement in his painting, although he took pride in his ability. In fact, Jean-Joseph himself had once painted on an old door in the house at Marnoz the picture of an aged soldier leaning against his spade in the open fields. But the thought of his son leading the uncertain life of an artist did not please him. "It was not for this that my grandfather bought us our freedom," he said to himself. Louis sensed his father's displeasure, and knew that it worried him to hear anyone in Arbois nickname him "artist." Jean-Joseph was a determined, somewhat obstinate man, and he would never give up hope that some day Louis might become a teacher.

Another person who exerted a strong influence on Louis was the headmaster of his school. Louis enjoyed walking about the school yard with M. Romanet, who had taken such a kindly interest in him. And the teacher, in turn, was not only impressed with Louis' diligence but with his flashes of enthusiasm and imagination. Louis' eyes sparkled when the headmaster told him about the Normal School in Paris which trained young men to teach in high school. Sometimes, he added, they even became university professors. He explained that the little Collège d'Arbois could not prepare him for the entrance examinations to the great Ecole Normale Supérieure in Paris.

"Paris!" thought Louis excitedly, did the headmaster really think he might go to Paris?

"And, Louis," he said, "before you can even take these examinations, you must have a bachelor's degree [more elementary than a bachelor's degree in an American college]. If you want to enter the science section of the Ecole Normale, you must first take your degree in Bachelor of Letters, then a year or so later, your degree in Bachelor of Sciences."

"How can I do all this? Where can I go?" asked Louis.

"In Paris," answered M. Romanet, "there is a good boarding school run by M. Barbet, who was born in Franche-Comté. It is called Pension Barbet. He takes special interest in any boy who is a Franc-Comtois, so he will be very interested in you. You will attend classes at the large Lycée St. Louis [a public high school]."

Jean-Joseph had dared to hope that Louis might some day become a teacher at the Collège d'Arbois, but M. Romanet had greater ambitions. "He ought to be a Professor in a great university," he told Jean-Joseph. And to Louis he said, "My young friend, try for admission to the Ecole Normale Supérieure in Paris."

The idea excited Louis. He wanted to go, but his father was reluctant to let his son, not quite sixteen years old, go to the great city of Paris, 250 miles way. Why not send him to the large Collège Royal (private high school) at Besançon, which was so much nearer home? Even if M. Barbet was a Franc-Comtois and would therefore take Louis at reduced rates, how could he afford to send him?

Finally, however, Jean-Joseph agreed to the Paris

school, and it was arranged that Louis should leave in
October, 1838. His school friend, Jules Vercel, would
also be going to Paris to study for his bachelor's degree.
What a relief to Louis' parents that he would not have to
take the long journey alone.

Although both boys had looked forward to this great
adventure, the actual leave taking was hard on that dark,
cold, rainy October morning. They climbed onto the
stagecoach and settled under a great tarpaulin behind
the driver's seat, for there was no room inside, filled as it
was with other passengers and all the baggage. With
heavy hearts, the two boys waved good-by. It was far
more difficult to leave their families, their friends, and
their little village than either country lad had ever
dreamed it would be.

The journey grew more and more strenuous as the old
stagecoach, drawn by five horses, splashed over the muddy
roads. They stopped at several towns to change horses,
and slept two nights in strange country inns. At last,
after traveling the 250 miles, they rattled noisily through
the narrow, stone-paved streets of a section of Paris known
as the Latin Quarter, where students and artists lived.

Louis, a tired and bewildered country lad, entered the
Pension Barbet. But he could not settle down to work.
He thought constantly of his parents, his sisters, and the
quiet little village of Arbois. Strange people walked the
streets of Paris, and queer noises filled the city. He could
not even get used to the smoky atmosphere and longed
to breathe the clear mountain air of the Jura.

He tried to reason away his loneliness, which left him

helpless in spite of his passion for study, his eagerness to work, and his determination to make the most of this great opportunity. He thought of how hard his parents labored and of how much they had sacrificed to send him away to school. Night after night he lay awake, and in the morning he would say to Jules, "If only I could get a whiff of the tannery yard, I feel I should be cured."

M. Barbet tried to cheer him, but each day his homesickness grew worse. At last, M. Barbet felt he must inform Louis' parents that he was worried about the health of their son. A few days later Louis received the mysterious message that he was wanted in a nearby café. There he found his father, who said simply, "I have come to fetch you." Each knew how lonely the other had been.

What joy to be home again! The Paris episode had been a great disappointment, but Louis went back to the little Collège d'Arbois with new energy. He entered the last and most advanced class, called the "form in rhetoric," which included the all-important subject of mathematics. He had so hoped to work in the "rhetoric class" at the lycée in Paris, but he settled down to the only plan now open to him.

He worked hard in school, and spent all his spare time drawing. He painted anyone who asked for a portrait— and there were many, old and young. An old barrel-maker with a wrinkled forehead dressed in a festive blue coat and yellow waistcoat, a lawyer with a wide collar on his frock coat, an old nun of eighty-two in her fluted cap, wearing an ivory cross, a sickly little boy in a velvet suit— all these and many more made up his portrait gallery.

Although the young artist received endless praise for his work, something was reawakening his ambition to enter the Ecole Normale Supérieure in Paris. For one thing, his school work was going better, and he was even taking many prizes. Perhaps most important of all, M. Romanet continued to encourage him.

By the end of the year Louis had finished all the studies the little Collège d'Arbois could offer him, and he knew that he must now leave home and study in a larger school. But where should he go? To return to Paris so soon again seemed frightening.

In those days, many boys took advanced study in Besançon, at the Collège Royal, which was only about 30 miles away from Arbois. Besides, Louis' father went to Besançon every month to the big fair in the market place, to sell his leather. They could see each other often. Everyone agreed that it would be a good decision to send Louis to the Collège Royal.

At Besançon the philosophy teacher inspired Louis, but the science master was dull. He was an elderly man who longed for the "good old days" when pupils did not ask so many questions. The students learned chemistry by rote from a book, and Louis' questions too often embarrassed the elderly teacher. Although Louis was still painting portraits, and still winning praise, he wrote home in January of that first year (1840) just after his seventeenth birthday:

... All this [success in painting] does not lead to the Ecole Normale. I prefer a first place at college to ten thousand superficial compliments in the course of conversation.... We shall meet on Sunday, dear father, for I believe there is a fair on Monday. If we see M. Daunas, we will speak to him of the Ecole Normale. Dear sisters, let me tell you again, work hard, love each other. When one is accustomed to work it is impossible to do without it; besides, everything in this world depends on that. With science, one is happy; with science one can rise above all one's fellows and it is good to see an educated young lady. But I hope all this good advice to you is superfluous, and I am sure you spend many moments every day learning your grammar. Love each other as I love you, while waiting the happy day when I shall be received at the Ecole Normale. I love you, my dear parents. Your devoted son,

Pasteur L.

Already, at an early age, Louis was beginning to follow the French custom in which the eldest son assumes the role of family guardian.

It was customary in those days to award prizes to the pupils at the end of the school year. At Besançon Louis received first prize for good conduct and application, a prize in drawing, second certificate of merit in theology and Latin, fourth certificate of merit in physics, and first in mathematics. In August he passed the examinations set by the government for the degree of Bachelor of Letters with the following record:

Greek (Plutarch) ..	GOOD	Medicine	GOOD
Latin (Virgil)	GOOD	Philosophy	GOOD
Rhetoric	GOOD	French Composition	GOOD
History	FAIR	Elementary Science	EXCELLENT
Geography	FAIR		

This was not an outstanding report, but the headmaster had selected Louis as a young man "most likely to succeed in life." He admired his youthful dignity, his seriousness of purpose, and his love of work. So, despite the fact that his record was not brilliant, he invited Louis to return the following year to Besançon as *preparation master*. This meant that he would help the younger pupils prepare their lessons and at the same time continue with his own. His board and room were provided, and in addition he received 300 francs. This seemed a lot of money to Louis, who wrote to his parents: "I assure you I am really not worth it." At Besançon, he was getting a good preparation for his degree of Bachelor of Sciences, but his mind was now constantly on Paris. "Paris," he said, "where study is deeper."

Louis had come to know and admire one of his classmates, Charles Chappuis, who was the son of a lawyer and a student in philosophy. Although Louis was beginning to think more and more about science, and Charles had settled on philosophy, they had much in common and shared each other's seriousness of purpose. Once in Paris, Charles wrote often to Louis. Louis answered with long letters, often assuring Charles that soon he would be able to join him. He was certain Charles would be admitted to the Ecole Normale, and he dared to hope that he would also.

By December of 1841, Louis' studies were going very well: he was first in his class in physics and second in mathematics. "If I had received such good marks two years ago," he wrote home, "I would have been elated." Finally, in the summer of 1842 he took his examinations for the degree in science. What irony that the young student who was destined to become the greatest chemist of his day received only "mediocre" in chemistry.

He was now ready to try his luck with the entrance examinations to the great Ecole Normale in Paris. He passed fifteenth in rank among twenty-two candidates. He could now enter this great institution and prepare to become a teacher.

For Louis Pasteur, however, fifteenth was too low. He withdrew his application to the Ecole, and decided to go back to Paris to the Pension Barbet, where he had so struggled with homesickness. He would attend classes at the Lycée St. Louis, and try again for a higher admission rating at the Ecole Normale.

Before leaving Arbois for Paris in the fall of 1842, Louis, who was not quite twenty years old, made his last painting—a portrait of his father. Jean-Joseph's sober expression and melancholy eyes are as sensitively drawn as was the character study Louis had made of his mother a few years earlier. Every detail noted by the observing artist is conscientiously included. This critical attention to detail was a trait which characterized all his later work as a scientist.

CHAPTER 3

Return to Paris

LOUIS WAS BACK in Paris. This time he had come with Charles Chappuis, and he intended to stay. Charles had been admitted to the Ecole Normale and Louis was a student at Pension Barbet. The two young men had missed each other during the previous year, when Charles had gone to Paris ahead of Louis, and both rejoiced that they were once more together. They were constant companions, sharing their deepest thoughts and their youthful ambitions. As Louis quaintly wrote to his parents: "Who is it that I am always with? Chappuis. Again who? Chappuis."

During the four years since Louis' first visit to the great city, he had grown taller, but for a boy almost twenty, he was still very short of stature. Now a bachelor of science, he was determined to advance as far as he could. He had learned that the entrance requirements to the Ecole Normale were very difficult, and that he could meet his own high standards only by working very hard. This would not be difficult, for he was happiest when absorbed in work. How far his interest in physics and chemistry would lead him, he could not tell, but he would push himself to the limit.

Charles was a very serious young man, and hoped some day to be a teacher of philosophy in a collège or a lycée. Although his own future was well mapped out, he knew that Louis, whom he so greatly admired, was still testing his strength, still waiting to see what the future would bring. But Charles was certain that his friend would go far.

Louis Pasteur settled into the Pension Barbet with a feeling of confidence and excitement. He would pay only one-third of his tuition fee, for he had been engaged to teach the younger pupils mathematics every morning between six and seven. He wrote to his father that he hoped these boys would come to love and fear him.

He did not live in the school, but shared a nearby room with two other pupils. There was little heat and the stone floor made the room very cold, so they rented a stove and bought some wood. But sometimes it was just too cold to study. Louis worked hard and helped M. Barbet in so many ways that he was soon excused from payment of all tuition fees. He wrote to his parents: "Do not be anxious about my health and work. I need hardly get up until 5:45, you see it is not so very early. I am always in bed before ten o'clock."

An affectionate and intimate correspondence passed between Paris and Arbois. Louis sent his sisters many presents, seldom forgetting little Emilie, who was now sixteen. Virginie and Josephine were proud to have their brother studying in the great city of Paris and counted the days between his letters. He urged them to study faithfully their grammar and inquired how Virginie was progressing with her music lessons. He wrote that he would "spend Thursdays in a neighboring library with Chappuis, who has four hours to himself that day. On Sundays we will walk and work a little together; we hope to do some philosophy on Sundays; perhaps too on Thursdays; I shall also read some literary works. Surely you must see that I am not homesick this time." The previous experience when his heart ruled over his will still weighed upon him.

Jean-Joseph worried lest his son be led astray by temptations in the Latin Quarter of Paris, and warned him against the dangers of the wicked city. Louis quickly disposed of such problems by answering: "Here more than anywhere else, virtue and vice, . . . wealth and poverty, talent and ignorance clash and cross. But when you have moral fiber, you can live here with as simple and upright a heart as in any other place."

As a student at the Pension Barbet, Louis attended classes at the Lycée St. Louis. In order to be admitted to the science section of the Ecole Normale, he was concentrating in chemistry, physics, and mathematics. There were about sixty highly selected students in the physics and mathematics classes, and Louis was greatly stimulated by the healthy competition and the superior teaching of his masters. He admitted to his parents that at Besançon he had neglected physics and chemistry, and that mathematics had actually bored him. Everything was different now.

His greatest inspiration, however, came from hearing lectures at the Sorbonne given by the celebrated chemist, Professor Jean-Baptiste Dumas. The Sorbonne, one of the most celebrated institutions for advanced learning in the world, is one of the endowed colleges of the University of Paris, which was founded in the eleventh century. Louis found it exciting living and studying in the very heart of the student section of Paris, with the Sorbonne just across the street from the Lycée St. Louis.

Professor Dumas had begun his career in chemistry in a humble way. He started as an assistant to an apothecary in a small town in southern France, where he was born. At the age of sixteen, he went to Geneva, where he still worked with an apothecary. While in Geneva, Dumas went to lectures in physics, chemistry, and botany and later assisted in the research work of professional scientists. Through them he became interested in the chemistry of living things, and it was not long before he was attracting attention among scientists by his own discoveries. These brilliant reports soon won him great fame throughout Europe and he was made professor of chemistry at the Sorbonne. This self-educated man, with no formal university degree, became one of the great chemists of the nineteenth century and the founder of organic chemistry, the chemistry of living things.

Jean-Baptiste Dumas was not only a great chemist, he was a great teacher and an influential government official who served on committees concerned with scientific problems related to society. In addition, he was one of the most eloquent speakers of his time. When he lectured

at the Sorbonne, hundreds came, not only to learn from
him but to witness the vigor and magnetism of his personality. He always lectured in a black suit, with a white
vest and black tie—a costume which added an official
note to his whole personality. His lectures were always
carefully prepared, and he spoke clearly and easily.
Standing before a large audience, he conducted experiments with masterly skill.

Louis was filled with admiration for Dumas, and he
went away from these lectures intoxicated with ideas
which not only showed him new vistas of what was known
but, still more important, opened unchartered areas of the
unknown. He wrote home: "You cannot imagine what
a crowd of people come to these lectures. The room is
immense, and always quite full. We have to be there
half an hour before the time to get a good place, as you
would in a theatre; there are always six or seven hundred
people."

At Besançon, Louis had recited his chemistry lesson by
rote from a book, and too often his penetrating questions
had embarrassed his teacher. In Paris he became the disciple of Dumas, who gave him his first glimpse into the
excitement of chemical research.

Louis found the study of acoustics, an entirely new subject in those days, very difficult. He took singing lessons
twice a week, not only to learn more about this art, but
especially to learn how to read musical notes. Quite
rightly he believed that this might help him to understand the physics of sound. He was taking advantage of
every opportunity which Paris offered.

Like many a young student away at college, he used up his allowance and asked for more money. His father, who had to economize on family expenses in order to send him money, scolded him for careless spending. Louis answered: "I have spent this year too much; this is all too true. I recognize it as you do, that if I had organized my expenses a little I would have had to ask you for less. But I have never spent large sums at any one time. My money has gone in spending 20 or 40 sous (cents) here and there. That's why it would be difficult for me to write out for you a budget of my expenses."

Then he listed some of the items which he could recall: paper, pen points, a book rebound, candles, a rented stove for his room, wood for the stove, a cloth for his table (so full of cracks and holes that it bothered him in writing), a cab to go to the home of a friend of his father's before he knew how to find the house, dinner every Sunday at Palais Royal with Chappuis (a plan his father had urged for relaxation), the theater three times and the opera once with Chappuis, sixty francs for an overcoat, sixty francs for his room, and tuition for music lessons. If this was too much, then he said that he did not know how to manage.

He reminded his "dear parents" that he had earned all his tuition at the pension and added that his future and theirs would be the better for the training he was getting. In all reasonableness he continued: "Even so, you are quite right in telling and scolding me for spending too much. This will make me more prudent without depriving me more than before, and I am honestly grateful to you for it. However, you didn't have to go wild about it, and you didn't have to work up such a bad temper against me."

Having dealt with the money question, Louis continued in an even more determined fashion concerning his education: "I have it on good authority that you have said that you were almost decided to make me come back from Paris, and that it wasn't necessary to go to the Ecole in order to become a teacher. In that you are horribly mistaken, and if you only knew the difference in all respects that there is between being a professor in a *collège royal* and *communal* [a large university and a small community high school], you would change your opinion. But for that, all you need to do is to talk to any teacher and you will see what he tells you."

Jean-Joseph had always hoped that his son might some day be a teacher in the little Collège d'Arbois. Now the matter was clear: Louis intended to reach the highest post. Father and son had disagreed, but Louis declared himself, and both respected and loved each other the more for it.

At the end of the school year, Louis took examinations set by the government for admission to the science section of the Ecole Normale. This time he stood fourth in rank. He had now met his own standards for admission. Had there ever been a young student more persistent in his quest for learning? All along the way he had received encouragement from home and guidance from those teachers who, in one way or another, had had faith in his ability. But no one at this time could possibly have predicted the marks of scientific genius that his work was soon to show.

Louis spent the summer of 1843 at Arbois and wrote to M. Barbet, offering to give lessons at the pension in his free time while studying at the Ecole. The headmaster gratefully accepted his offer and added in his formal style that, "It will indeed be a means of frequent intercourse between us, in which we shall both find much advantage."

In his eagerness to return to Paris and enter the Ecole Normale, Louis arrived several days early and was allowed to sleep in an empty dormitory. He went at once to see M. Barbet, and it was arranged that he would come regularly at six o'clock on Thursday afternoons and give the boys a lesson in physics. Jean-Joseph was pleased that Louis had volunteered to help M. Barbet, who had been so kind, and wrote: "You should do so, not only for your own sake, but for others; it will encourage him to show the same kindness to other studious young men, whose future might depend upon it."

Louis, a grave, quiet, shy young man, now faced three years of concentrated study at the Ecole Normale to prepare himself to be a science teacher. He concentrated in all branches of advanced physics, chemistry, and mathematics. Although he hoped to teach one or more of these subjects, courses in the methods of teaching or the philosophy of education were unknown in those days. Whatever he learned about the art of teaching came from observing the methods of the great masters with whom he studied.

He did all his work with meticulous care, was never

able to "skim" when reading a book, and all his notes were taken in his small, very fine handwriting.   And what a pile of lecture notes he had.   He studied mathematics and chemistry at the Sorbonne, and mathematics, physics and chemistry at the Ecole Normale.   All in all, he attended about twenty hours of lectures each week. Added to this, he spent every Tuesday afternoon in the chemistry laboratory working with others under the direction of a teacher.   And finally, there was one hour of laboratory work every day, in which he learned the techniques of glass blowing, carpentry, and metalwork.   Scientists of 100 years ago had to make much of their own special apparatus, so that these instructions were essential. He wrote his parents about courses in English and German which he planned to take.   If he took only one, he said he preferred English, for it would be easier to find a German teacher when he found he needed to read German.

The Ecole was a small state institution of only a few hundred highly selected students who paid no tuition. Thousands attended the Sorbonne, where a fee was charged for each course.   Louis' main task was to learn all he could about physics, chemistry, and mathematics.

Chemistry in those days was a young science.   People were concerned with discovering how to substitute one element for another in different compounds.   For example, how could the sodium in sodium chloride (table salt) be replaced by calcium or ammonia?   How could one change sodium chloride into ammonium chloride? As Pasteur described these studies, he said that chemical substances were like "molecular edifices, in which one element could be replaced by another without disturbing the structure of the edifice; as if one were to replace, one by one, every stone of a monument by a new stone."

The newer and bolder an idea, the more it excited Louis, and yet practical work in the laboratory brought him closer to the experiences of experimentation. One day a professor lectured on the techniques of obtaining phosphorus from bone. Merely to hear about it did not satisfy Louis' yearning to see for himself. So he bought some bones, took them to the laboratory, burned them to a fine ash, and proceeded to extract the element. He finally obtained sixty grams, and placed the substance in a small vial labelling it "phosphorus." What a joy this was to have gone through the experiment, step by step, all on his own.

From his professor of mineralogy, Louis learned about crystals, which are the form most substances take when in the pure, solid state. He loved this study, for it appealed to his unusual ability for observing the smallest detail, and in the study of crystals he had to measure their angles with a special magnifying instrument called a goniometer. For example, when a pure salt solution evaporates, sodium chloride crystals appear as tiny, perfect cubes, and each angle measures exactly 45 degrees. Louis soon came to love crystallography above all his other studies.

Jean-Joseph knew that Louis was studying all day and late into the night and that he often spent Sundays in the laboratory working alone on some project. Louis' father wrote often to Chappuis and always urged him to be sure that Louis did not overtax himself. Every Sunday afternoon, Charles would go to Louis' laboratory and patiently wait for him to finish some experiment. Finally, partly cross but mostly grateful to Charles for waiting so quietly, Louis would take off his apron and say, "All right, let's go for a walk."

Time and time again they went to the Luxembourg Gardens, which are not far from the Sorbonne. In the spring, they often sat on benches near the flowering horse-chestnut trees. In the summer they watched little children play with their tiny boats in the central pond; and in the winter, Charles and Louis walked briskly up and down the long, straight paths that ran in a mazelike pattern between the frozen gardens. Overlooking this great stretch of gardens stands the Luxembourg Palace in all its ancient glory.

But Charles and Louis paid little attention to their surroundings, for they were absorbed in discussing some philosophical point Charles had heard the day before in Professor Simon's lecture, or Louis talked about some experiment he was doing. One day as they started off for a walk in the Luxembourg Gardens, Louis said to himself, "How can I demonstrate polarized light to Charles?" And as he left the laboratory he may well have slipped a crystal of calcium carbonate, known as Iceland spar, into his pocket.

They entered the gardens and walked along the paths. Behind them stood the Luxembourg Palace, its windows brilliantly reflecting the light from the setting sun. Handing the crystal to Charles, Louis said:

"Now I'm going to show you the great discovery that the French physicist, Malus, made about forty years ago. Take this crystal, turn around and look through it at the sunlight reflected from the palace windows."

"Yes," said Charles, holding the crystal to his eye and looking through it at a sunlit window, "I can see the light through the crystal."

"Now Malus happened to turn the crystal very slowly while looking through it at those very same windows," said Louis excitedly, and Charles began slowly rotating the crystal.

"It gets dimmer and dimmer, and now it's bright again," said Charles in astonishment.

"That's exactly what Malus saw," answered Louis, "and he explained the fact by saying that the crystal blocks certain rays and allows those traveling in one particular plane to pass through it. When you hold the crystal at a certain angle, it screens out almost all the rays, so that you see almost no light coming through. If you were looking through a piece of glass instead of this crystal, the light would never get dimmer no matter how much you turned it."

Then wishing to make the main point of this demonstration clearer, Louis added:

"Some of the sun's rays go through the window, of course, but some do not and are reflected back toward us. The crystal you hold analyzes those reflected rays, and showed Malus that they were all traveling in only one plane. When that plane coincides with the plane in the crystal, the rays go through it and you see a bright light, but when the crystal is held at right angles to this plane, almost no light comes through and it appears very dim. Malus called light traveling only in one plane *polarized light,* and it was he who discovered that light reflected from a smooth surface—like the window—*is* polarized. We were lucky, and so was Malus, that the reflected rays were traveling at just the angle to be analyzed by the crystal."

"You said that instrument you were using in the laboratory when I came in this afternoon was a polarimeter?" queried Charles.

"Yes," answered Louis excited to see that Charles was so interested. "A polarimeter has two crystals in it. Ordinary light from the gas lamp I was using goes through the first crystal which polarizes the light. The second crystal analyzes those rays, just like the one you are holding up to the polarized light reflected from the Palace windows. I am learning to test the effect different chemicals have on polarized light."

Louis told all about Malus with as much excitement as though he himself had discovered that the reflected light was polarized, and Charles always marvelled at his friend's ability to make things clear and interesting. As they started back home, Louis could not refrain from saying:

"The question which excites me most right now is one raised by a report from the great crystallographer Mitscherlich. He claims that two acids are chemically alike in every way, yet they have different effects on polarized light."

"But why is this so exciting?" asked Charles.

"It seems to me illogical that two substances can be so

exactly alike and yet behave differently in respect to polarized light. There must be some difference either in
their crystals, or in some other way that no one has yet
discovered."

As they continued their way along Boulevard St.
Michel, Charles said to Louis:

"What a pity you have to study for your examinations
at the Ecole and have so little time for research. You
might be the person to discover that difference."

"Don't worry about that now Charles," answered Louis,
"I'll work on my examinations, then I'll study for my
Doctor of Science degree. With this accomplished, I can
become a professor of chemistry like Dumas, and then do
research."

Pasteur's classmates, who nicknamed Louis "Laboratory Pillar," were also working hard preparing for the
examinations. When time came to take them, a number
of them surpassed him. Louis ranked seventh in the
license examination, and the next year, fourteen students
were ready for the *agrégation* (highest examination for
selecting professors). Four of them passed and Louis
ranked third. He could now be nominated by the
government to some teaching post.

Few *Normaliens* sensed Pasteur's hidden trait of genius,
but Chappuis knew only too well his friend's power of
concentration and his zeal for attacking the unknown.
Once Chappuis said, "You will see what Pasteur will be!"

M. Balard, Professor of Chemistry at the Ecole, was
another who was well aware of Pasteur's dedication to
work. So when the Minister of Public Instruction wished

to send Louis to teach physics in a high school in a small town some hundred miles from Paris, Professor Balard intervened. It seemed to him utter folly to bury a promising young scientist, eager for research, in a time-consuming teaching position in a small school. Balard's pleadings carried weight, and Louis became his assistant at the Ecole Normale. His salary was small and his duties were slight, for he had merely to prepare chemical materials for Balard's laboratory and for the demonstrations that Balard gave when lecturing. Louis had plenty of time to complete the work required for his degree of Doctor of Science.

Professor Balard was an eccentric man of forty-six who made a fetish of leading a life of stark simplicity. When he traveled, his only luggage was a shirt and a pair of socks which he wrapped in a newspaper and slipped into his pocket. He had two laboratory rooms of his own at the Ecole. In one of them he had his bed, not so much to sleep near his work as to carry out his idea of the simple life. In fact, Balard had done little original work since his discovery of bromine when twenty-six. His strength lay in stimulating others to research. He worshiped simplicity to such an extent that he actually rejoiced when he saw Louis compelled to fit a delicate measuring device into his microscope to make his goniometer. Balard brought his students up on the philosophy of Benjamin Franklin, whom he was forever quoting: "A good workman knows how to file with a saw and saw with a file." This was the atmosphere in which Louis started out on his own research.

As Balard's assistant, Louis attended some advanced

chemistry courses at the Sorbonne given by Dumas. Each year, this great teacher had inspired Louis more and more, and one day despite the fact that he had never met Dumas, he wrote to him asking for a position as an assistant teacher at the Ecole centrale, a new institution founded by Dumas.

Paris, 7 November, 1846

Monsieur,

Allow me to write you a request. This year I finished work at the Ecole Normale as an agrégé in physical sciences, and at the suggestion of M. Balard, I have become curator in chemistry in this institution. . . . I have a great desire to give part of my time during my stay in Paris to work in the difficult art of teaching. I will tell you with a frankness, perhaps too naive, that it is my ambition to become a distinguished professor.

[He then told of the number of institutions where he had thought he might gain experience in teaching, and added]

Then I have had the idea that perhaps at the Ecole centrale you might need an additional assistant in physics or better still in chemistry, and I come to offer myself to you. . . . You will probably excuse the boldness of my request if you recall the time when you aspired to the talent of a professorship. I am too young to have seen your beginnings, but surely you have not arrived suddenly at the summit that you have reached; once you must have hoped very much to obtain a teaching post which would make it possible for you to climb to heights which you now command.

Dumas was not able to give Louis Pasteur the position he so much wanted. But the attention of the noted chemist had certainly been caught by this candid, almost bold letter, and future events were to make it impossible for Dumas ever to forget the young man who had written it.

Chappuis left Paris and went to Besançon as a teacher

in philosophy. Louis' letters to him were filled with enthusiasm at working with Balard, and by the end of the year 1847 he had completed all requirements for his degree as Doctor of Science. He dedicated his essays for this degree to his father and mother, and after they had been printed, sent them a copy. Jean-Joseph wrote: "We cannot judge of your essays, but our satisfaction is no less great. I was far from hoping as much; all *my* ambition was satisfied with the 'agrégation.' "

Although the son had gone far beyond the father's fondest hope, Louis Pasteur's scientific career had not yet begun. His unusual powers of concentration, his active imagination, and his dedication to work were all driving him toward scientific frontiers that no one had ever crossed.

CHAPTER 4

First Hint of Genius

CHEMISTS in the days of Pasteur were interested in studying the hard, crusty deposits that formed inside wine barrels. Wherever a Frenchman could grow grapes, he grew them, so that all along the countryside of southern France there were barrels full of wine, all rimmed with red or yellow deposits. For hundreds of years wine makers had seen this crust, but what it was did not concern them because it appeared regardless of whether the wine turned out to be good or bad.

In 1770 a Swedish chemist analyzed these crusty masses and extracted a pure white substance which he called *tartaric acid,* a natural substance in the juice of grapes. As the wine aged and evaporated, tartaric acid crystallized out along with various colored sediments.

Gradually, wine makers came to know that this crusty deposit contained tartaric acid which, indeed, had many uses. It was employed in dyeing and in printing calico. "Cream of tartar," which is acid potassium tartrate, was used in baking. Most important of all, the tartrates had medicinal value. The shelves of apothecary shops were filled with bottles of different tartrates, because physicians were writing prescriptions containing this or that tartrate for this or that ailment. These prescribed medicines effervesced when mixed with a glass of water just as "cream of tartar" causes bubbles to rise in cake dough as it bakes. Effervescing medicines became quite the fashion. To meet these various demands, chemical factories worked hard making different compounds of tartaric acid.

Louis Pasteur became interested in tartaric acid because his teachers were. They were trying to discover all the different substances that would react with it. Their concern was primarily theoretical, or so they thought. Actually, they too were following a fashion, for the demands of society determine what a scientist chooses to study more than he realizes. However, these research scientists were really trying to find out all they could about the chemistry of the tartrates, unmindful for the moment of the practical value their discoveries might have.

It was therefore quite natural that crystallographers were studying the shape and form of tartrate crystals. Pasteur loved the study of crystals above all else, and one might have predicted that sooner or later he would be trying to unravel some mystery hidden in these crystals.

When Louis had studied about tartrates in chemistry, he learned that in the early part of the nineteenth century, an Alsatian chemical manufacturer, while making tartaric acid, had found, by mere chance, a new and curious acid. But try as he might, he could not make it again. A few years later, the great chemist Gay-Lussac visited the factory, studied the properties of the new acid, and named it *racemic,* meaning grapelike. Sometime later it was called *paratartaric* acid. It resembled tartaric acid and yet was strangely different. Just what this racemic acid was seemed shrouded in mystery.

When Louis had told Charles about polarized light and about the two acids that Mitscherlich claimed were identical yet acted differently when tested in the polarimeter, he had been talking about tartaric and racemic acids. Mitscherlich had reported that the specific gravity, the melting point, even the chemical structure of these two acids were identical, and yet curiously enough, their effect on polarized light was different. He claimed that, when polarized light was passed through a solution of tartaric acid, the beams entered at one angle and came out of the solution at another angle. That is, a solution of tartaric acid "twisted" the beams of polarized light and was therefore *optically active.* As for racemic acid, the rays passed through unchanged. That is, there was no "twisting." For this reason, racemic acid was called *optically inactive.*

Louis had thought about Mitscherlich's report for more than a year. It excited him because he found it illogical, and therefore he doubted it. As he said: "A profound incompatability exists between Mitscherlich's discovery of the different relationship of these two tartrates toward polarized light, and his statement that they are identical in every respect."

Now that Louis had his Doctor of Science degree and served as Balard's assistant, he had time for research. He also had the imagination and the audacity to challenge the logic of the famous German crystallographer. The more he pondered the problem, the more it excited him. He shut himself up in Balard's laboratory and began working day and night.

He had to use a polarimeter to determine the optical activity of these acids. Although this instrument was not a new invention and was used by several scientists throughout Europe, Pasteur had to make his own, and probably proceeded in somewhat the following way. He had learned how to work with metal, and so he made a long cylindrical metal tube. He used two crystals of Iceland spar, each cut to form a Nicol prism. Such a prism permits only certain rays of light traveling in one plane to pass through it, thus polarizing this light.

Pasteur firmly fitted one prism inside one end of the metal tube and made it lighttight, and similarly he fitted the other prism inside the other end. The second prism, however, could be rotated. That is, it could be placed at exactly the same angle as the first or it could be rotated to the right or to the left. The long metal tube with its two Nicol prisms was then firmly supported on iron rods so that it stood about 5 or 6 inches high when placed on a table. This was his polarimeter. Now how did he use it?

To test the effect of racemic and tartaric acid on polarized light, Pasteur made a solution of each substance, which he proceeded to test separately. He poured the test solution into a glass container which fitted into the metal tube. The only light entering the polarimeter came from a gaslight placed just outside and beyond the first prism. He looked through the second one to see if and how the light, polarized by the first prism, passed through the solution and on through the second prism.

With the moveable prism at exactly the same angle as

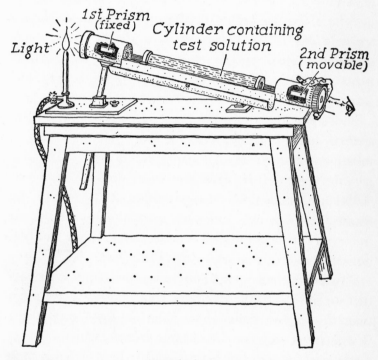

A polarimeter

the stationary one, did the light come through it? If it did, the solution Pasteur was testing had no effect on polarized light and was called *optically inactive*. If he could see no light, he moved the second prism to the right—or to the left—until a bright beam was visible. If he had to move the prism to the right, he said that the solution was *right-rotary*. If he had to move it to the left, it was *left-rotary*. By noting just how much he had to move the second prism, he could measure the degree to which the solution had rotated polarized light to the right or to the left.

There was no doubt about it. A solution of tartaric crystals *did* rotate polarized light to the right. The racemic solution had no effect whatever; it *was* optically inactive. "Then," reasoned Pasteur, "the *crystals* of these two acids must differ."

With fine forceps, he picked up each tiny, dry, tartrate crystal and put it under the microscope. Suddenly he made an observation that had escaped even the critical eye of Mitscherlich: each and every crystal had a very small face, or facet, which appeared on one side only! Because there was only one such facet, the crystal was not symmetrical. He called it *asymmetrical*. How had Mitscherlich ever missed seeing this little facet?

"Now I have it," said Pasteur to himself, as his imagination pushed on to the next idea. "Since these asymmetric tartrate crystals rotate polarized light to the right, I will surely find that the racemic crystals, which are optically inactive, will not have this little facet—they will be symmetrical." This hunch then became the hypothesis which he put to test by carefully examining the racemic crystals.

What a shock it was, when carefully examining each racemic crystal under the microscope, he saw that they too had the same little facet just on one side. They, like the tartrate crystals, were asymmetrical, and he said, "For an instant my heart stopped beating." Was he after all on the wrong track? Would all this lead nowhere?

Louis' active imagination came to the rescue. He had the ingenious idea of taking each crystal of racemic acid and orienting it with reference to a plane perpendicular to himself. Then he saw that the confused mass of crystals could be separated into two groups: one group had

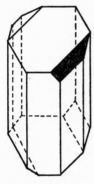 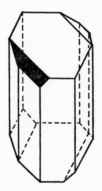

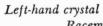
Left-hand crystal   *Right-hand crystal*
Racemic-acid crystals

the little facet on his left side, and in the other group, the facet appeared on his right. Here was the secret. Racemic acid was made up of two kinds of crystals: one type was asymmetrical to the right and the other asymmetrical to the left.

Pasteur then quickly realized that when a crystal from one group was placed before a mirror, an *image* of the crystal of the other group was seen—just as the right hand, when seen in the mirror, gives an image of the left.

No matter how much a person's two hands may look alike, they are not identical—the glove of one hand will not fit the other hand.

Racemic acid, therefore, was made up of two different types of crystals, a right-hand type and a left-hand type. The crystals in one group were mirror images of those in the other. Natural tartaric acid occurring in grapes contained only right-hand crystals. Mitscherlich was in error. Tartaric and racemic acid were not identical in every respect.

Now for some final crucial tests to clinch the story.

One by one, Pasteur picked up each racemic crystal. Into one pile he put the right-hand forms and into another pile the left-hand forms. Then he reasoned, "Since the right-hand crystals of natural tartaric acid turn polarized light to the right, the right-hand racemic, or para-tartrates, should do similarly, and the left-hand ones should deviate the light to the left. Furthermore, in a solution made of equal weights of the two types of crystals, the two effects should cancel out each other, and thus explain why racemic acid is optically inactive. If this is true, all is clear."

With great excitement and some anxiety he put his predictions to test.

They worked.

"I have it!" he exclaimed and ran out of the laboratory. In the corridor he bumped into a chemistry assistant, threw his arms around him and exclaimed, "I have just made a great discovery. I am so happy that I am shaking all over."

Louis had for the first time in his life pioneered across a scientific frontier from the known to the unknown. Lost in the mysteries of little crystals and their facets, he had found not only the secret of racemic acid, but also the thrill of scientific research. It was as though some hidden spark of genius had suddenly been lighted.

The news of any scientific discovery of great importance travels fast. This was as true 100 years ago in Paris as it is today throughout the world. Pasteur's discovery of right- and left-hand racemic crystals became the topic of the day among scientists in Paris. The famous chemist, Dumas, listened thoughtfully. Professor Balard, in whose laboratory Pasteur had done his work, eloquently praised the discovery. However, the seventy-two-year-old Professor Biot, who years ago had made a name for himself in chemistry and crystallography, was skeptical. Biot could not believe that so young a doctor of science—in fact, a mere student only twenty-six years old—could have solved a problem too great for Mitscherlich. As Biot listened to the talk of different scientists, he said, "Are you quite sure? I would like to investigate that young man's results."

Pasteur took the initiative and wrote to Biot asking for a conference. Biot answered, "I shall be pleased to verify your results if you will communicate them confidentially to me. Please believe in the feelings of interest inspired in me by all young men who work with accuracy and perseverance."

The two men met at the Collège de France, where Biot lived. The elderly man presented Pasteur with some racemic acid saying, "I have most carefully studied it. It is absolutely neutral in the presence of polarized light."

Pasteur had made his tests with crystals of compounds of the acid: ammonium and sodium racemate. Biot handed Louis some soda and ammonia, and asked him to prepare the solutions then and there in his presence. Then Biot poured the solutions into a crystallizer and placed it in a corner of his room where he could be certain it would remained undisturbed.

"I shall let you know when you are to come back," he said, bidding him good-by.

Forty-eight hours later, a few very small crystals began to form. These increased in size, and when enough had appeared, Biot asked Pasteur to return. In his presence, Pasteur separated the crystals one by one, placing them in two piles, and showed Biot the left-hand and right-hand ones.

"So you affirm," said Biot, "that your right-hand crystals will deviate to the right the plane of polarization, and your left-hand ones will deviate it to the left."

"Yes," answered Pasteur.

"Well, let me do the rest," and once more he bid Pasteur farewell.

Biot proceeded to make separate solutions of each type of crystal—a solution of the left-hand ones and a solution of the right-hand ones. Again Pasteur was called. In his presence, Biot selected the left-hand tartrate solution, for this would be the critical test. Placing it in the polarimeter, he gave one look and knew that Pasteur was right. He seized Louis' arm and exclaimed, "My dear boy, I have loved science so much during my life that this touches my very heart!"

Any scientific discovery must pass the critical examination of any competent expert. Louis' first piece of original research stood up well against such a test.

Pasteur's curiosity carried him far beyond the discovery of right- and left-hand crystals. "What does this mean?" he asked himself. Again his active imagination had a ready answer. He thought that the form of any crystal was determined by the architectural pattern of the molecules in it. He said that he did not know just how the atoms in tartrate molecules were arranged, but he was certain that the molecular structure possessed three dimensions. Furthermore, he believed that this structure was asymmetrical, so that if it were possible to place the molecule before a mirror, it would give an image of itself which would not fit over it—again, like the glove of the right hand not fitting the left.

These predictions soon stimulated experiments of other scientists, who later, but within Pasteur's lifetime, laid the foundation of that branch of chemistry which today is known as stereochemistry. It is a field of science which investigates the *spatial* arrangement of atoms in a molecule—an arrangement of them in three dimensions rather than in two.

Pasteur was right in thinking that the shape of a crystal is determined by the form and shape of the molecules in it. He could not tell, however, what this arrangement is by knowing the shape of the crystals, nor could he know that years later scientists would discover that by exposing

crystals to special X-ray analyses, their molecular structure can be determined. Thus it was, that the work done
about ninety years ago by a young man of twenty-six
stimulated other men to develop one of the most important branches of modern chemistry. Any piece of work
which stimulates others to carry the quest further has met
one of the highest tests of greatness.

In this first scientific adventure Pasteur showed his unusual skill as an experimenter. He had the necessary requirement first to recognize an important question and
then to be able to translate it into practical experimental
tests. As he once said, "To know how to wonder and
question is the first step of the mind toward discovery."

In the midst of Louis' work on crystals, France was
stirred by new political upheavals—the Revolution of
1848. King Louis Philippe was taking sides with his
Premier, Guizot, who refused to make concessions to the
demands of the people. Reform was demanded, Paris was
in turmoil, and King Louis Philippe fled to England
never to return as King of France. Louis Pasteur's pa-
triotic spirit was stirred with visions of the birth of the
Second Republic, and with the magic of the words—
liberty, equality, and *fraternity.*

Jean-Joseph, seeming to have forgotten his own feelings
of patriotism when fighting for Napoleon I, wrote to
Louis on February 20: "I pray you, my dear child, do
not leave your room. I know I do not need to warn you
to stay away from all political demonstrations."

The Second Republic was promptly proclaimed, and
a temporary government was established with the poet

Alphonse de Lamartine as one of its leading members. Louis and many others enthusiastically greeted the idea of a poet-politician as leader among men.

By April, the government called for volunteers to fight off rioters who were trying to crush this idealistic uprising. Louis joined the National Guard, and wrote:

> Paris, Sunday, 16 April, 1848
>
> My dear parents:
> .... I am writing from the Orleans Railway, where as *garde national* I am stationed.... I am very happy that I was in Paris during the February days, and that I am still here; I should be sorry to leave Paris just now. It is a beautiful and sublime doctrine which is now being unfolded before our eyes. I am getting accustomed to the noise of conflicts, of riots, and if I had to, I would fight with the greatest courage for the holy cause of the Republic.

Jean-Joseph violently disagreed and answered at once:

> ... If you feel that you owe something to law and order in Paris, you owe two hundred thousand times more to your family; never lose sight of that fact. Therefore, in any kind of riot stay home; that is where you belong.

By May, the rioting in Paris was over, and Louis returned to the Ecole Normale and to his crystals. Only a few weeks passed, however, when he received the greatest blow of all. Word came that his mother had suddenly been taken very seriously ill. He dropped everything and rushed to Arbois, but arrived too late to see her before she died.

Life in the old tannery was completely changed. Jean-Joseph, who by nature was a melancholy man, could not speak. Virginie and Josephine went about the house grief-stricken, and Emilie seemed lost without her mother. The one person who had brought gaiety into this happy, yet somber, household had left them. Jean-Joseph became more than ever absorbed in his own thoughts.

Louis could not bring himself to return to his work at the Ecole, and a week after his mother's death, he wrote to Chappuis; "My poor mother is dead. She succumbed in a few hours, and when I arrived she was no longer in our midst. I may not return to Paris this year; I shall ask for a vacation."

There was one topic which Jean-Joseph and Louis never dared talk about. Each feared that his mother's anxiety over Louis' safety during recent months in Paris might have caused the heart attack which had snatched her from them.

CHAPTER 5

The Impetuous Lover

LOUIS REMAINED in Arbois during the summer, torn between wanting to get on with his career and wishing to comfort those at home. They longed to have him there, but everyone was aware that Louis was restless to get back to the work he loved. No one pressed him to stay, but where should he go? What should he do?

His salary as Balard's assistant was very small. He could live on it and be happy with his crystals. But he aspired to be a "distinguished professor" in a university where his teaching would be a challenge and he could have time for research. He sent to Paris for his books, and wrote to Chappuis that he planned to prepare a course in chemistry, lesson by lesson. But he found that he could not work in the old tannery with his mother gone. Thoughts of Paris pressed upon him day and night.

Balard and Biot were the teachers most interested in Louis at this time. How different his two sponsors were: Professor Balard, the spirited eccentric bustling about the laboratory, following the work of his students with noisy enthusiasm, and Biot, the elderly, quiet, retired professor who stood aloof even from his colleagues. For Louis, however, Biot was beginning to develop almost a fatherly affection.

Balard would have liked nothing better than to keep Louis as his assistant, and Biot was eager to follow Louis' experiments with his crystals wherever they might lead. But both men knew, and Louis knew, that his next step would be dictated by the government, which had complete authority. It directed the curriculum at the Ecole Normale, solicited and selected the students, and after their graduation, placed them in teaching posts. Each student upon entrance signed an agreement to teach at least ten years after graduating.

Louis left Arbois for Paris in September, knowing that there was no vacancy for a professor of science in any university. To his great disappointment, he soon learned that he had been nominated to teach physics at Lycée de Dijon near Dôle in southern France. He would have seven or eight classes in elementary physics, no time for research, and he must report for duty by the first of October. His sponsors intervened, and the Ministry of Education permitted him to remain in Paris an extra month.

Louis spent these precious days with Biot at the Collège de France. Together they drafted his report on right-hand and left-hand racemic crystals to be read at the Academy of Sciences. With great pride, Biot himself would present Louis' work, thus giving status to the first achievement of so young a scientist.

Biot was outraged that the government did not recognize the importance of Louis' research on crystals. For years he had tried to interest chemists in the value of studying rotary polarization, and now to take Pasteur away from these investigations was a personal blow to this aged and distinguished scientist.

"If at least," he said to Louis, "they were sending you to a Faculté [government institution for advanced study]. They don't seem to realize that such labors [Louis' research] stand above everything else."

But the Ministry of Education looked at everything in a practical way. In Dijon there were pupils who needed a teacher, and besides, how could these money-conscious government officials be expected to understand the importance of little crystals that had tiny facets? So Louis went to Dijon.

Although he was bored at the lycée, he was eager to prove himself a good teacher and carried out his responsibilities in the conscientious way in which he did everything. He wrote to Chappuis:

I find that preparing my lessons takes up a great deal of time. It is only when I have prepared a lesson very carefully that I succeed in making it very clear and capable of compelling attention. If I neglect it at all, I lecture badly and become unintelligible.... Don't you think that it is a mistake not to limit classes to fifty boys at the most? It is with great difficulty that I can secure the attention of all toward the end of the lesson. I have found one means, which is to multiply experiments at the last moment.

Louis was hopeful that some day he would receive a better appointment, for he knew that his teachers in Paris were working in his behalf. But he never dreamed that it would come so soon. He had been at the lycée only three months when a vacancy in chemistry occurred at the University of Strasbourg, in Alsace, a region in France close to the German border. He was first made assistant professor and later was promoted to full professor of chemistry, with time and facilities for research. He spent the next five years there—perhaps the happiest period of his life.

M. Bertin, Professor of Physics at the University, was an old friend of Chappuis, and Louis had known him when the three were students in Paris. Bertin had always admired Louis' simple and honest nature and quickly welcomed him to Strasbourg saying:

"First of all, you are coming to live with me. You could not do better. It's only a stone's throw from the Faculté."

Bertin was a successful teacher who took great personal interest in his students. In the home of this jovial man, Pasteur's life became gayer and more varied. The hearty and carefree Bertin was a good companion for the tense, serious-minded Pasteur, so lacking in humor.

"Oh, Bertin," sighed Louis one day, "if only I had your wit."

For nine years Louis had lived in dingy student rooms, first at Besançon, then in Paris. At times he had wanted the comforts of a home life, and once he had written to his father that, since he did not intend to marry for a long time, he wished that one of his sisters might make a home for him. His father had answered that he wished so too, for his sake as well as for his sisters', because "neither of them wish for a greater happiness. Both desire nothing better than to look after your comfort. You are absolutely everything to them."

Jean-Joseph himself regretted that Louis had not yet married, and in one of his letters he repeated a comment of a friend. "Your son is in the best position to make a brilliant marriage, and no doubt, like so many others, does not realize it. . . . I beg you to suggest early to him that he has but to ask in order to obtain." Jean-Joseph had never placed too much emphasis on money; yet he was a shrewd man and a hard worker. He knew the things that money can bring and he hoped for a "brilliant" marriage that would bring wealth to his son, who was becoming famous.

When Louis had thought of his sister making a home for him, and when Jean-Joseph had suggested that he might marry for money, neither one was taking into account the fact that Louis Pasteur was by nature a deeply romantic young man. They had also forgotten the phrase which people had used about Louis' mother, Jeanne Roqui, when they saw her devotion to Jean-Joseph. For generations there had been a saying about the Roquis which characterized his mother, and which Louis was soon to discover in himself. To his amazed delight, he found that he, too, could "love like a Roquis."

At the University of Strasbourg, M. Laurent had just been appointed the new president. He had begun his career as a teacher in a lycée, but his unusual administrative abilities soon won him the honor of numerous promotions as director of various schools which needed reorganization.

When Louis paid his first official visit to the home of

the new president, he at once felt at ease in the comfortable modest dwelling, although it was of such a different social background from his own. Mme. Laurent's forebears had been literary people. Her father had been a printer and her mother had owned a bookstore where, at certain hours in the day, booklovers gathered to discuss modern writers. How different had been the ways of Pasteur's forebears, who had lived as tanners and tillers of the soil. But Louis' parents had valued the good things in life, and in his humble home he had developed a high moral sense and learned to look upon life in an exalted way. Here in the president's home, he sensed this same atmosphere.

At Strasbourg, members of the faculty of the university found a cordial welcome in the home of M. and Mme. Laurent. She was a warm-hearted, modest person intent on helping her husband in every way she could. They had three daughters: the oldest was married, but the two younger ones added much gaiety to the popular Sunday-evening parties at which the faculty gathered.

On a cold winter night Louis went with Bertin to his first Sunday evening party at the president's house. They entered a large library where books lined the walls and a small piano stood at one end. They joined a group of faculty men standing near a fire that was burning brightly in an open grate. Marie Laurent, the president's second daughter, was the center of attraction, gaily recounting some recent amusing episode. Bertin interrupted:

"Mlle. Marie, may I present our new professor of chemistry, M. Pasteur?"

From the first moment that Marie met and talked with Louis, she was attracted to him—he was so quiet, so shy, and so serious. She had been educated at a pension where one of the teachers had had a profound intellectual and religious influence on her, and now at the age of twenty-two, she had become an extremely devout Catholic. There was a kind of noble dignity in Louis that strongly appealed to her religious nature.

As for Louis, he had fallen in love with Marie at first sight. He may have seemed shy, but when Louis was certain about anything, he had never been one to deliberate. Since the first moment he had seen her, he had been deeply moved by a mixture of kindness and courage that he sensed in her. He delighted that she seemed so learned, and he loved her gaiety and her bright blue eyes. He had always loved his mother's merry spirit and had often heard her sing, but never had her singing made him as happy as did Marie's that evening when she sat at the piano singing old familiar French songs.

During the next week he thought constantly of Marie, remembering exactly how she looked, all her charming gestures and everything she had said. How his heart had leaped when he had heard her sing and play. For the first time he realized how lonely he had been, and now he knew that never before had he been so happy. He could not wait for the next faculty party, and when he went the following Sunday, not a doubt remained. He loved Marie Laurent.

Louis Pasteur could not wait to declare his love. He spoke with no one, not even Bertin. Of course, he must

follow the French custom of making his formal proposal
of marriage to her father before having any word with
Marie.　But as for waiting—he could not and did not.

Two weeks after first meeting Marie, Louis sent the
following quaint letter to President Laurent asking for
his daughter's hand in marriage, unable to put into words
the depth of his feeling for Marie:

Strasbourg, 10 February, 1849

Sir—

An offer of the greatest importance to me and to your family
is about to be made to you in my behalf; and I feel it my duty to
put you in possession of the following facts, which may have some
weight in determining your acceptance or refusal.

My father is a tanner in the small town of Arbois in the Jura.
I have three sisters.　The youngest suffered at the age of three
from a cerebral fever which completely interrupted the development of her intelligence.　She is mentally a child, although adult
in body.　We expect to place her shortly in a convent where she
probably will spend the rest of her life.　My two sisters keep house
for my father and assist him with his books, taking the place of
my mother whom we had the misfortune to lose May last.

My family is in easy circumstances, but with no fortune.　I do
not value what we possess at more than 50,000 francs, and as for
me, I have long ago decided to hand over to my sisters the whole
of what should be my share.　I have, therefore, absolutely no fortune.　My only means are good health, some courage, and my position at the University.

I left the Ecole Normale two years ago, an 'agrégé' in physical
science.　I have had a Doctor's degree eighteen months, and I
have presented to the Academy a few works which have been very
well received, especially the last one, upon which a report was
made which I now have the honor to enclose.

This, Sir, is all my present position.　As to the future, unless
my tastes should completely change, I shall give myself up entirely
to chemical research.　I hope to return to Paris when I have ac-

quired some reputation through my scientific labors. M. Biot has
often told me to think seriously about the Institute; perhaps I may
do so in ten or fifteen years' time, and after assiduous work; but
this is but a dream, and not the motive which makes me love science for science's sake.

My father will himself come to Strasbourg to make this proposal of marriage. No one here knows of the project which I
have formed and I feel certain, Sir, that if you refuse my request,
your refusal will not be known to anyone.

Accept, Sir, the assurance of my profound respect, etc.

P.S.—I was twenty-six on December 27

Marie could hardly believe that true love might burst
forth almost at first sight and was as surprised as her father
at the suddenness of this proposal. President Laurent was
shocked. How could he, in two short weeks, possibly
know this impetuous young man? Although Marie had
been attracted to Louis the moment she met him, she now
began to mistrust her feelings and prayed to know the
secret of her heart. Days went by, and no word went out
to her suitor.

Louis wrote to his father about Marie and told him of
his letter to President Laurent. Jean-Joseph forgot his
hopes for a "brilliant" marriage and remembered only
his love for Louis' mother. About two weeks later Jean-
Joseph and Josephine went to Strasbourg. The two
fathers met, the proposal was made according to the best
French tradition. Jean-Joseph returned to Arbois, but
Josephine remained with Louis.

Louis' only other confident was, of course, Chappuis, to
whom he wrote: "What ideas one gets in the province.
Here am I thinking about getting married; I, who intended to wait until I was thirty years old. It is serious,

and it is very probable that I will marry one of the daughters of M. Laurent, President of the University of Strasbourg, if I am accepted.   I have already talked with my father."

But Marie needed more time.   That she loved Louis she no longer doubted, but a decision of such importance could not be made at once.   The suspense in waiting, however, became more than Louis could bear.   For the first time since the death of his mother, when for weeks his grief had made work impossible, he now lost interest in his research.   His lectures were going badly.

Feeling that Mme. Laurent was his ally, he wrote to her: "I am afraid that Mlle. Marie may be influenced by early impressions, unfavorable to me.   There is nothing in me to attract a young girl's fancy.   But my recollections tell me that those who have known me very well have loved me very much."

If the truth be known, Louis Pasteur was a most attractive young man, with jet-black hair and a short, neatly trimmed black beard.   He always dressed with great care, and wore small, rimmed spectacles, for he was nearsighted.   There was something appealing about his sad eyes and kindly expression.

Having received permission to write to Marie directly he said: "All I beg of you, Mlle., is that you will not judge me too hastily, and therefore misjudge me.   Time will show that below my cold, shy and unpleasing exterior, there is a heart full of affection for you."

Louis had written asking just the hour of what days he might go to see Marie.   If he could know this, he said, he

might be able to settle down to work. Marie urged him
to come at any time—as often as he could. His visits
became more frequent. Often they saw each other daily.
Sometimes Josephine went with him, sometimes he went
alone.

Louis told Marie about Paris and his love for the great
city. "I dream of going back there sometime in an important position. It has always been an ambition for
myself alone. Now, it is an ambition I have for us," he
told her.

"And I love Paris, too," answered Marie in all truth and
simplicity.

"Then you, too, would like to live there?" he asked.

"Oh, yes, Louis," Marie assured him.

Louis had feared that Marie would feel lost in the great
city and was overjoyed to find that Paris held no fears for
her.

When Marie had seen Louis with his father and heard
them talk together, she soon knew that he was what she
called a true "family" man. This made her especially
happy. She liked the gentle way Louis and Josephine
spoke with each other, and they always made her feel as if
she, too, belonged. When she had asked him about Emilie, she at once felt his affection for the poor little sister
who was so handicapped. All Louis' kindness came out
whenever he spoke of his home and his family, and it was
then that she could see Louis as father of her own children.

One day after leaving Marie, Louis seemed to remember
that he had done all the talking. He had told her about
Biot and racemic crystals. Had he talked too much? But

she had seemed so interested and had asked so many questions. Had she really understood that crystallography is
very important, or had he just lost himself in his own enthusiasm? Why was it that she could not yet say she would
marry him?

A few more weeks dragged by before one day Marie said:
"Louis, if I marry you, I must marry science, too. I must
love you so much that I will also love science. Sometimes
I think I do; then another time I'm frightened that it is
only you I love."

In saying this, in sharing her fears, she suddenly felt
closer to him than she had ever felt before. Louis saw all
her radiance return. She was gay again, and they laughed
together about how serious they had been. Marie's courage, which he so needed, had come back, and he sensed it
just as he had the first time they met. When Louis left her
this time, he knew that her love for him ran as deep as his
for her. He wrote to her at once: "My dear Marie, now I
am confident that you will love me. Thanks, a thousand
thanks for your love. I was so restless. . . . I have only one
thought: you."

So it was that on May 29, 1849, only three months after
his proposal, Marie Laurent and Louis Pasteur were married as they knelt before the altar in the French Catholic
church of St. Madeleine in Strasbourg.

From now on the story of Louis Pasteur is that of a life in
which Marie Pasteur shared in all his successes and all his
trials. From the very beginning, she insisted that the
work in the laboratory should come first. She followed his
researches and helped him write his reports, always urging

him to make clear to her some point he was trying to get across to his reader. One of Pasteur's pupils said of her, "She was not only an incomparable companion to her husband, but also his best collaborator."

She also forgave him all his absent-mindedness, so amusingly described by Chappuis upon one occasion when Louis Napoleon Bonaparte, the nephew of Napoleon I, who had been elected President of the Second Republic, visited Strasbourg to be royally entertained. Upon this festive day, when people in the neighborhood marched in procession led by banners, Pasteur returned to his laboratory "for a few moments," but paid no attention to the passage of time. Mme. Pasteur waited in vain for him to return, and missed the whole celebration. When Pasteur came home in the evening, she had no word of reproach when he said simply, "I could not interrupt my experiments."

It was also Chappuis who said that it was Marie who deserved the credit for accepting Louis as a husband, "such as he was, with his habit of living in his laboratory, with his passion for work, and his tendency to be absorbed in thought, and for having never turned him from his course, or been too jealous of science."

CHAPTER 6

From Lifeless Crystals
to Living Microbes

LOUIS PASTEUR and his wife spent the next five years in Strasbourg. It seems miraculous that neither the joys nor the sorrows that filled their family life interrupted his pursuit of science. His name became better and better known through his continued work with crystals. His lectures at the university were very popular, for he spoke with eloquence and enthusiasm. He was rapidly becoming a true disciple of Dumas.

April 2, 1850 marked the birthday of their first baby, whom they named Jeanne in memory of Louis' mother. No matter if there were lectures to prepare, reports of his research to be written, or laboratory experiments to be finished, never a day went by that Louis did not find time to play with little Jeanne or help his wife to care for her. He was even a better "family" man than Marie had ever dreamed he could be.

The young couple met sorrow too, when tragedy again hit the home in Arbois. Soon after Josephine returned from Louis' wedding, she developed a serious lung disease and died seven months after the birth of little Jeanne. It had been only two years since Jean-Joseph had lost his wife, and now Josephine, who had tried to fill her mother's role in the home was taken from him. Although Louis felt her loss deeply, his sympathy went to his father who, as Louis wrote to Chappuis, was now "desolate." He said that he would willingly join Chappuis at Besançon, if only to be nearer his father.

That same year, President Laurent was dismissed from the University of Strasbourg purely for political reasons. Every faculty member was shocked, and Pasteur was outraged, but no one could combat the intrigues existing between various government groups. Rather than accept an inferior appointment, President and Mme. Laurent went to Paris, where he retired. Marie and Louis now felt they had three homes: their own modest one in Strasbourg, the old tannery in Arbois, and the new home in Paris.

A few months after Louis' marriage, Biot had reported Pasteur's work on racemic crystals at a meeting of the Academy of Sciences. Now, a year later, Louis himself lectured in Paris at the Academy on his latest studies of crystal formation and rotary polarization. Dumas and Biot were present, each watching him with closest attention, not missing a single word. After the meeting, Biot drew Louis aside and said, "My young friend, that was as good as it possibly could be."

Dumas wanted to know better this young man who had four years previously written that almost bold letter asking for a teaching post that would help him become a "distinguished" professor. Dumas now paid Louis the compliment of inviting him to his home. The two men talked about crystals and more crystals. As Louis was about to leave, Dumas said:

"You prove to me that when a Frenchman takes up crystallography, he knows what he is about. If you persevere in these studies, you will be the founder of a new branch in chemistry."

For some time, France had led other nations of Europe in the science of crystallography, and Louis Pasteur played an important role in further establishing this national reputation.

A few weeks later, at another meeting of the Academy, Biot evaluated Pasteur's work, and there was no one in all of France better qualified to pass such judgement. He praised the delicate precision shown in Louis' research and concluded, "Pasteur throws light upon everything he touches."

Louis had complained to Chappuis that his latest work contained no new, big ideas. It was just an extension and verification of his first work on racemic acid. How fast did Louis expect *big new ideas* to be born in one brain?

Pasteur returned to Strasbourg, to his wife and little Jeanne, who was "growing like a mushroom," and to his crystals. He turned to the study of malic acid (found in apples) and aspartic acid (found in seedlings). He extracted these acids in the pure state, and analyzed their chemical composition. He studied the shape of their crystals, which he made by allowing solutions of these acids to evaporate. Low and behold, these crystals were also asymmetric—they had little facets just on one side. He must carefully preserve all the crystals he made, protect their facets from chipping, and show them all to Biot.

When summer vacation came, Louis made plans to go to Paris. Jeanne was too small to take to the great city unless her mother could go also. But Marie wished to stay at home because in a few months she expected to have another baby. So Louis begged his father to join him in Paris, for he wanted them both to forget that unhappy visit thirteen years earlier when the father had gone to fetch his homesick son.

Jean-Joseph was delighted at any chance to be with Louis, and since life at the old home at Arbois was easier, he felt free to leave. Emilie was living in a convent not far from Arbois. Virginie had married, and she and her husband made their home in the old tannery. Jean-Joseph's son-in-law helped in making leather, and Louis rejoiced that his father, who was now almost sixty years old, need not work so hard. Both father and son looked forward to this short holiday together in Paris.

Mme. and Professor Biot welcomed Louis and his father into their home as they would have received few others. Jean-Joseph was touched by all their kindness, and when he returned to Arbois he wrote thanking them for all they were doing for Louis and sent a basket of fruit from his garden—the only gift he had to offer the distinguished scientist who continued to take such a deep interest in his son. Biot answered: "It is the greatest pleasure that I can experience in my old age, to see young men of talent work-

ing industriously and trying to progress in a scientific career by means of steady and persevering labor. . . . That is
what has made your son dear to me, and his affection for
me adds yet to his other claims and increases that which I
feel for him. We are therefore even with one another."

Biot and Louis studied the collection of new crystals.
They talked about the meaning of their shape and form.
They theorized about the structure of the molecules of
malic acid that gave shape to its crystals, and the different
molecular pattern of aspartic acid which gave its crystals a
still different shape. They both realized that Louis was
revolutionizing crystallography—raising it from a descrip-
tive science which merely classified crystals and making it
a tool for chemical research. The study of crystals might
some day help chemists to discover the way atoms unite to
make molecules.

Louis returned to Strasbourg. When November came,
little Jeanne, who was about eighteen months old, had a
baby brother, Jean-Baptiste, named for both Biot and
Dumas. The parents' joy at having a son was complete
when Professor Biot consented to act as godfather. Marie
was as pleased as Louis, for she had developed a real affection for this elderly gentleman who was doing so much
for her husband.

When Jean-Baptiste was only a day old, Pasteur held
little Jeanne's hand and helped her walk to the baby's crib.
Then he took her in his arms so that she could see her baby
brother, but it would be some weeks before she would be
able to say "Batitim," a nickname his parents soon gave
him.

Jeanne had always been a very healthy baby, but Jean-Baptiste was frail and often cried for hours at a time. Jeanne cried sometimes too, because she was still cutting her teeth. Jean-Joseph worried lest Louis might lose patience with all these domestic trials, but Marie wrote to her father-in-law: "You are wrong in assuming that Louis is beginning to be irritated by the crying of the two children. He is a model of a family father, who even though he works hard, finds a way of spending a moment of every day at the crib of the infant, and to take care of the little girl when I cannot do it."

Despite domestic happiness and tribulations, Louis wrote to Chappuis when Jean-Baptiste was only a few weeks old that he was on the verge of great mysteries and "the veil which covers them is getting thinner and thinner. The nights seem to me too long, yet I do not complain, for I prepare my lectures easily, and often have five whole days a week that I can devote to the laboratory. I am often scolded by my good Marie, whom I console by saying that I shall lead her to posterity." He was constantly thinking about racemic acid: why was it so scarce, and why had no one recently been able to find it?

During the summer vacation of the following year, Pasteur took his whole family on his annual pilgrimage to Paris. Marie and the children stayed with her parents and Pasteur settled in a nearby hotel. Almost upon arrival, he took Marie and "Batitim" to see Biot, who later planned a surprise for Louis.

Pasteur had come to Paris laden with numerous crystals. One day, he found a note at his hotel from Biot: "Please come to my house tomorrow at 8 A.M., if possible with your products. M. Mitscherlich and M. Rose are coming at nine to see them."

What an honor! Louis would meet two of Germany's great crystallographers, one of them none other than the same Mitscherlich whom he had dared to challenge eight years previously. How cordial would this meeting be?

Louis went to the Collège de France bright and early that Sunday morning. Biot believed that the meeting would go well, as indeed it did. Rose and Mitscherlich praised Pasteur's work, studied his collection of crystals, and all four men became so lost while discussing the mysteries of these tiny forms that two and one-half hours passed before anyone realized it.

Two days later, Louis went to a large dinner party at the home of a French baron. All guests present were members of the Academy of Sciences. Louis was the only outsider.

During the gaiety of the dinner conversation, Louis' attention was caught when he heard Mitscherlich say to someone, "But there is now a chemical manufacturer in Germany who is making racemic acid."

Louis' mind was sent racing: he must see this factory.

"They say that tartrates used by this manufacturer," added Mitscherlich, "came originally from Trieste."

"I shall go to Trieste," declared Louis turning to Mitscherlich, "I shall go to the end of the world. I *must* discover the source of racemic acid. I must follow up the tartrates to their orgin." And go he did.

First, however, the matter of collecting 1,000 francs to support his travels had to be settled. With characteristic impetuosity, Louis begged Biot and Dumas to help him. Surely, he thought, the sum could be obtained from the government, or from the Academy. Delays increased Louis' impatience and Biot had to prevent him from writing to the President of the Republic.

"But France should consider it a point of honor to support such a project," insisted Louis.

"But it is not necessary to set the government in motion for this," answered Biot with a twinkle.

It was impossible to calm Louis. Finally, Marie's married sister, Mme. Zevort, loaned Louis the money. Dumas agreed to reimburse him upon his return, and off Louis started that first week in September, 1852. Marie wrote to her father-in-law, "There are many annoyances in this affair, because we do not know how or when we ourselves can repay Mme. Zevort. But we have the word of M. Dumas, . . . and M. Biot will not abandon us. All that I desire is that Louis may be successful."

Pasteur set forth with the determination of a detective tracking down a lost jewel, for he was actually hunting out the hiding place of the precious substance that had started him on his road to fame. He met and questioned many chemists and manufacturers in Leipzig, Freiberg, Vienna, and Prague. Some thought they had made racemic acid, only to be shown by Pasteur that they were mistaken. He met chemists in some of the universities and was surprised to discover that even in Germany his name was already known. In some cities he was given the use of chemical laboratories, where he worked late into the night on collected specimens.

He wrote long letters almost daily to Marie, sending

endearing messages to Jeanne and "Batitim," whom he was already calling his "dear little chemist." He carefully gave Marie his itinerary so that she might write to him. His letters told how carefully he was spending his money, how much his simple meals and lodging cost. Jean-Joseph had not looked with favor upon this trip. *Germany* was no place for his son to go. Louis wrote Marie that his father need not worry that he would lose his way, and when he returned he would tell his father that, after all, he was a man thirty years old and could be relied upon.

Louis' first trip outside France was broadening his outlook on life in many ways. He found no language difficulty, for he could speak some German, and he was surprised that his German colleagues spoke French so easily and were so well-informed about France. He was pleased to be received with such friendliness and respect. He visited some art galleries and museums and made careful notes in a little diary that Mme. Laurent had given him about the paintings of the old masters that most pleased him. It was a trip that Marie would also have enjoyed, but there was no complaining. This project was very important to Louis, and if he reached his goal, if he found racemic acid, then she could happily remain in Paris with her parents and her two children.

Louis was progressing with his detective work, and began to formulate a conclusion which he tested wherever he went. Finally, it became clear that during the manufacturing process of purification of crude tartaric acid, racemic acid was always present in the *mother liquor,* the fluid which upon evaporation gives "birth" to the formation of its crystals. As the process of purification progressed, less and less racemic acid could be found with the true tartaric acid. He had found the precious substance, but the chemistry of its formation was still shrouded in mystery.

His vacation was over, and he was homesick and penniless. From Leipzig, he wrote to Marie, "I can at last turn my steps toward France. I want it; I am very weary." It had been four long weeks of separation for Marie. For Louis it had been an exciting and successful adventure, and so Marie was happy.

On October 7 Louis was back in Strasbourg. Chappuis was there, and together they went at once in search of a house where Louis' family could live. This was not an easy task, for there were four of them, and they hoped to have a maid to help Marie with the children and the household duties. They would have to plan carefully, for Louis' salary was small. Finally he wrote to Marie that he had found a suitable place and gave detailed instructions of just how she must travel. They should take a night train so that they could sleep on the long, twelve-hour trip, and they must obtain a first-class compartment. It was getting cold, and she should bring a blanket or rug to keep her feet warm. Little "Batitim" could sleep on a pillow beside her. He would meet them early in the morning, noting just the hour the train left Paris and its time of arrival in Strasbourg. He added in a humorous vein that, if she did not travel first class or if she arrived cold, he would send her back to Paris.

Marie was a capable young mother quite able to manage

everything, but she liked his attention to all these details.
By early October the little family was united again. They
spent three or four days at a hotel waiting for their new
home to be made ready and warm to receive them.

It was only a matter of a few days until Louis was deep
again in his teaching and getting things ready for work
in the laboratory. He had only discovered the hiding
place of racemic acid. It was not enough to describe its
presence as a manufacturing accident, and he would never
be satisfied until he himself could make it at his chemist's
bench.

In November he was promoted to a full professorship at
the university, which made his position secure and his salary larger. On January 3 of the following year, one entire
meeting of the Academy of Sciences was spent discussing
all of Pasteur's work. As a result, at the age of thirty-one
he received the red ribbon of the Legion of Honor from
the French government. Father and son had won the
same distinction in very different ways—the father for
distinguished service in the army of Napoleon I, the son
for solving mysteries hidden in little crystals. But both
saw their work as adding to the glory of France.

As the cold winter settled down upon the provincial city
of Strasbourg, Louis Pasteur spent every spare moment in
his laboratory trying to make racemic acid. He must somehow prepare it by starting with tartaric. Because no one
had ever been able to do this, and because racemic acid
might be found to have many uses, the Pharmaceutical
Society of Paris offered a prize of 5,000 francs to the first
person who might prepare it. Pasteur worked on the

problem all winter, not so much to win the award, but rather to satisfy a passionate desire to solve this mystery. As the months dragged on, he tried out one hunch after another, and he often said to himself, "I fear I am attempting a task which some chemists, including myself, have at times believed was impossible."

Suddenly one day in May he had the idea—where it came from he probably could not have traced—of making a special compound of tartaric acid. He would prepare the tartrate of cinchonine (similar to quinine) and expose the compound to intense heat for several hours. No sooner had the idea occurred to him than immediately he went to work, for this was the way he always functioned. He made it, he exposed it to intense heat, he allowed the hours to pass, he examined it—he had it! Off went the following telegram:

M. BIOT, COLLÈGE DE FRANCE, PARIS. I TRANSFORM TAR-
TARIC ACID INTO RACEMIC; PLEASE INFORM M. DUMAS AND
M. SENARMONT.

L. PASTEUR

At once he wrote to his father telling him the news, repeating the telegram and adding: "Here is at last that racemic acid (which I went to seek in Vienna) artificially obtained through tartaric acid. I long believed the transformation impossible. This discovery will have incalculable consequences."

But Biot had to have proof that Louis had actually accomplished this great feat and wrote that very day begging him to answer one question: Was the racemic acid he had made exactly the same in every respect as that which they had worked on together? Was it composed of right-hand and left-hand crystals?

Pasteur assured him that it was exactly the same. It did contain right-hand and left-hand crystals. Many rejoiced, especially Biot and Dumas, when the announcement of Pasteur's achievement was later made at the Academy of Sciences. More important than winning the pharmaceutical award, he had won a battle of great importance to himself personally and to the progress of science.

Pasteur spent the money from the award to purchase new instruments which the university could not afford and to pay the salary of a laboratory assistant. If Marie thought of other ways in which the money might have been used—and well she may have—she knew no *better* use. As always, the laboratory came first. When she had declared her love for Louis, she had said that it meant that she would love science too.

During the years at Strasbourg, Pasteur seemed almost chained to his crystals, but his mind was free and was pushing him on to problems far beyond them. Once when he had broken a crystal and put it back in its mother liquor, he noticed that as it increased in size, the greatest activity occurred around the damaged edges. As he watched the crystal "grow" and assume its original shape, he thought, "How this reminds me of the healing of wounds in the body. Broken crystals, like injured tissues, heal and are restored to their original form." His thoughts were beginning to carry him toward the mystery of living things.

A spectacular discovery of great importance followed.

One day in the laboratory, he happened to find a solution of tartaric acid covered with heavy growth of a greenish mold. Most chemists would have thrown the solution down the sink as worthless. But not Pasteur. It gave him an idea. He transferred the mold to racemic acid, allowed it to grow and then put the resulting liquid in the polarimeter. What effect did the growing mold have on the optically inactive racemic acid? Would the solution still have no effect on polarized light? To his amazement and intense interest, the solution now turned polarized light to the *left*. This must mean that the right-hand molecules in the racemic acid had disappeared, leaving only the left-hand ones. What did all this signify?

Contrary to the belief of chemists of those days, it meant only one thing to Louis Pasteur. It meant to him that the growing mold had selected only the right-hand molecules to feed upon; the left-hand ones remained untouched—undigested. What a beautiful example of a chemical change wrought by a living organism. The mold—a microscopic living plant (a microbe)—had grown and increased in number by "eating" only those molecules that were right-rotary.

"How strange," he thought, "that this microscopic plant should be so selective about what it eats. Microbes *must* bring about chemical changes. Microbes could be used to separate chemical substances." Had he not seen them separate right-rotary from left-rotary tartaric acid? Microbes could be used as a new tool in chemical research. Louis was bursting with big ideas and his crystals were actually forcing him to think about life. But these were only hunches, and in the years to come he would have to prove them to the satisfaction of other chemists as well as to himself.

On October 1, 1853, little Cécile was born, adding to the joys and responsibilities of the Strasbourg home. But Louis had not been taking care of his health: he had been working too feverishly for too many months and refused to recognize the warning signals of serious fatigue. Marie and her father became very concerned and M. Laurent wrote to Dumas asking him to use his influence in obtaining a few months leave for Louis. A substitute was found to take Louis' teaching, and he was granted leave with full salary.

With his family, he spent the rest of the academic year of 1854 in Paris living near the Luxembourg Gardens. He spent an hour or so each day quietly conferring with Biot, and when the weather permitted, he walked through the gardens with Marie or with little Jeanne or "Batitim." How things had changed from the days when he and Chappuis had shared their youthful ambitions strolling through these same paths.

Madeleine, who had been their maid in Strasbourg, came with them and helped in caring for the family, which now consisted of three very young and very healthy children: Jeanne who was almost four, Jean-Baptiste about two and a half, and four-months-old baby Cécile. Pasteur discovered during these months of relaxation that he could "play" as hard as he could work. His health was slowly returning and his leave was extended until the summer vacation.   By September he was back in full swing.

During the summer he had learned that the Ministry of Public Education wished to nominate him professor of chemistry and dean of the newly organized Faculté of Sciences in Lille, in northern France.   What should he do? He had fully expected to return to Strasbourg.   He must talk this over with Biot.

"Never before," said Biot, "have I known a young man of thirty-two to be appointed dean.   This is a most unheard of honor.   Of course, you intend to accept, do you not?"

"My work at Strasbourg has gone well, and Marie and I are so happy there.   It was in Strasbourg that we found each other," Louis answered thoughtfully.

"But Lille is the richest industrial city in northern France," continued Biot.   "Its distilling factories are having trouble in the manufacture of alcohol from beet sugar. The city needs a strong, flourishing scientific institution. They need you."

At home that evening, Marie asked, "Louis, what do you *want* to do?"

"It's hard to leave Strasbourg.   They have done so much for us," said Louis.

"But if Professor Biot urges you to go, it is for your sake and for the good of France.   I am ready to go with you," returned Marie.

This was all Louis needed.   Marie had the courage to try the new.   He would make the Faculté of Sciences at

Lille the best scientific institute outside Paris, reorganize the courses, arrange for new teachers, direct the construction of new buildings, and go to Lille ahead of his family to make plans for where they might live.   He could not wait to begin.

But what about his crystals?   These lifeless forms had already led him to wonder about the mysteries of life, and his appointment at Lille became the next stimulus to his own researches, which from now on would contribute more directly to the welfare of mankind.   They would deal with the science of making and preserving wine, and later with the cause and prevention of disease.   Pasteur's move to Lille was a turning point in his whole career.

CHAPTER 7

Putting Microbes to Work

IMPRESSIVE EXERCISES installing the young dean of the newly created Faculté of Sciences took place on December 7, 1854. In his opening speech, Pasteur enthusiastically described two new procedures. Students would be able to work in laboratories and carry out experiments described in lectures, and those wishing to become foremen in factories could study for a new, special diploma to be granted after two years of study. It was clear to all present, especially to manufacturers and their sons, that the young dean was eager to direct the teaching in the new school toward the solution of industrial problems. The city of Lille needed his help.

Marie was in Paris with the children waiting until Louis could find lodgings for them at Lille, and she missed the excitement of his inauguration. But when she read his speech, she could see how directly he had spoken to them:

Where in your family will you find a young man whose curiosity and interest will not immediately be aroused when you put into his hands a potato, when with that potato he may produce sugar, with that sugar alcohol, with that alcohol ether and vinegar?

103

Where is he who will not be happy to tell his family in the evening that he has just been working out an electric telegraph? And, gentlemen, be convinced of this, such studies are seldom if ever forgotten. It is somewhat as if geography were to be taught by traveling; such geography is remembered because one has seen the places. In the same way your sons will not forget what the air we breathe contains when they have once analyzed it, when in their hands and under their eyes the admirable properties of its elements have been found.

Marie also recognized the value he placed on theoretical work when he warned them not to think only of the practical applications of science:

Without theory, practice is but the routine of habit. Theory alone can awaken and develop the spirit of invention. It is essential that you should not share the view of those limited intellects which despise all science which has not immediate practical application.

He went on to tell them the story about Benjamin Franklin, who was in Paris in 1783 as minister for the new United States of America. As Franklin witnessed various balloon ascents made in France for the first time, a bystander asked, "What is the use of this?" Franklin answered: "What is the use of a newborn baby?" Pasteur concluded, "A theory has only one merit, that of existence. It awakens hope, that is all. But tend it, let it grow, and you will see what it will become."

What, indeed, has become of man's first ascent into space by a balloon made nearly two hundred years ago?

When Louis Pasteur went to Lille, he carried with him the theory that many chemical changes which scientists were studying were the result of microbes feeding on dif-

ferent substances. For instance, when milk sours, or fer-
ments, the change is the result of microbes feeding upon
milk sugar, lactose. Microbes use part of the lactose to
multiply and grow, and the part they do not use they dis-
card as lactic acid which sours the milk. So the acid has
been "put" into the milk by the microbes growing in it.
Pasteur tended these theories, let the ideas grow, step by
step, proof by proof, until his work was once more being
discussed among scientists throughout Europe.

A few weeks after Pasteur's inauguration, Marie came
to Lille with "Batitim" and Cécile. Jeanne went to Or-
leans to stay a few months with her grandparents, the Lau-
rents. Louis and his family took temporary lodgings waiting the completion of an apartment for the new dean in
one of the school buildings. On the floor below this apartment, he had his own laboratory. Life was ideal, for although he spent much time arranging new courses in
chemistry, physics, natural history, practical mechanics,
and geometry, he himself gave only one weekly lecture in
chemistry. He could easily escape almost any time of day
or night to work in his own laboratory.

One day, M. Bigo, the father of one of his students, came
to him for help. He was having trouble in his factory in
manufacturing alcohol from beet sugar. This production
of alcohol from beet sugar, which is called fermentation,
sometimes, for no known reason, turned out badly. Instead of making pure alcohol, the product they obtained
was sour. The chance of doing this manufacturer a kindness and the possibility of reporting new discoveries to the
students who were crowding his popular lectures excited

Pasteur. He made daily visits to the factory, discussed every step in the process with M. Bigo, brought back hundreds of samples to his own laboratory for careful study under the microscope. As Marie wrote to her father-in-law: "Louis is now up to his neck in beet juice. He spends his days in the alcohol factory. He has undoubtedly told you that he has only one lecture a week, which gives him much time, which he uses and abuses."

His microscope gave him the clue. When the manufacture of alcohol was successful, he saw millions of tiny oval globules, but when the product turned out badly and tasted sour, there were millions of another kind of microbe. These latter ones were much smaller and harder to see—but Pasteur spotted them. They were tiny, long rods.

Pasteur had the solution. The globules were the yeast cells—one kind of microbe—which fed upon beet sugar, and as they "ate" it, they discarded alcohol. He watched these globules grow by forming little buds which broke away from the mother cell as they grew bigger. Then they in turn formed buds themselves. The long tiny rods were bacteria—another kind of microbe. These grew very long and thin and multiplied by splitting into two tiny rods. When they contaminated the beet sugar, they made lactic acid, which soured the whole product.

Bigo's son worked with Pasteur through all the many weeks spent in making this discovery and wrote, "This very simple method [microscopic detection of rods] allowed us to watch the process and to avoid the failures in fermentation we used to meet so often." Chemists had not

thought of using the microscope in their fermentation
studies.   Now the alcohol factory could not succeed without one.

Yeast cells
showing budding

That chemical changes were brought about by living
microbes was a revolutionary idea in those days.   Dumas
looked upon fermentation as strange and obscure.   Liebig,
a leading chemist in Germany, insisted that microbes were
not responsible for fermentation.   Just as Pasteur had

Lactic-acid bacilli showing
division by splitting

challenged Mitscherlich, so now he opposed Liebig and
other chemists of his day who claimed that the presence of
yeast in fermenting fluids was the *result* of the process—not
the *cause,* as stated by Pasteur.

Liebig accepted the fact that yeast was always present during the fermenting of grape juice to make wine, but pointed out that in the fermentation of milk, that is, as it soured, yeast was absent. Therefore, he argued, if yeast contributed anything to the production of alcohol in fermenting grape juice or beet juice, it did so because it was *dead*—not because it was alive. He claimed that on dying, the yeast cells released a substance which caused sugar molecules to vibrate and split up into molecules of alcohol and carbon dioxide. Vague as this notion was, it had become the official dogma. It appeared in all the textbooks and was taught in all the universities.

Not only was Pasteur challenging the great chemist Liebig, he was expressing ideas which ran against the spirit of the times. Chemistry was the ruling science. Its methods were precise: from a known weight of sugar, one could predict the exact amount of alcohol which could be recovered. To bring the riddle of life into chemistry, seemed unnecessary and undesirable.

In comparison, biology was an infant science. Yeasts and molds were studied only by a few botanists, who were mainly interested in discovering what they looked like under the microscope. As a chemist, Pasteur was daring to ask: "What do these microbes do?" He had the training to describe what they did in chemical reactions. Pasteur was bringing chemistry to the riddle of life. With such a training, with his hunch that microbes were responsible for fermentations, and with all his intellectual fighting energy, he proceeded to fight Liebig point by point.

Pasteur directly attacked Liebig's statement that living

yeast could not produce alcoholic fermentation because milk fermented, or soured, without them, by first looking at a drop of sour milk under the microscope. He saw millions of tiny, rod-shaped forms, similar to those he had seen when alcohol had soured. It was true that milk fermented in the absence of yeast, as Liebig had stated, but its souring was due to a different microbe feeding on milk sugar and producing lactic acid. This other microbe was a lactic-acid-forming microbe. It was a little rod, a bacterium.

To establish his proof, Pasteur realized that he must isolate this rod and grow it in pure culture, that is, free from any other kind of microbe. He succeeded in growing it pure in plain, sterile broth. When he put a drop of this broth seething with lactic-acid-forming bacteria into a large quantity of milk, the milk became sour. It was now filled with lactic-acid-forming germs. In other words, as the lactic acid increased in amount, the milk became more and more sour, and the tiny rods increased in number. By this single stroke, Liebig's argument lost all its force.

Pasteur's first paper on the subject, entitled "A Memoir on Fermentation Called Lactic," upheld the "germ theory of fermentation," and was presented to the Lille Scientific Society on August 6, 1857. By first presenting his studies to Lille rather than to the Academy of Sciences at Paris, he gave recognition to the provincial institution where he had done his work. This classic report, which gave birth to the science of microbiology, did not reach the Academy in Paris until three months later.

Liebig still clung to his theory that fermentations were brought about by dead and decaying matter. From some poorly conducted experiments, it was discovered that ammonia sometimes appeared in fermenting fluids. Since it was known that decaying matter produced ammonia, Liebig seized upon these experiments to support his theory of the role of dead matter in fermentation reactions. Pasteur met this idea by growing yeast in a liquid of pure water, sugar, minerals, and ammonia.

The living yeast cells increased in numbers and produced alcohol. They actually fed upon the ammonia, for it was their only source of nitrogen. In other words, in Pasteur's carefully controlled experiments, ammonia did not appear as a product of dying yeasts. Instead, it supported their growth. This crucial test was decisive, and within a few years the microbe theory of fermentation was generally accepted.

These theories became established because they worked, and in time Pasteur was able to produce whatever fermentation he wished by selecting the appropriate organism. His skill made it possible for him to produce fermentation of alcohol, or of lactic acid, acetic acid, citric acid, or butyric acid—this last which is responsible for rancid butter. The theories of Liebig had not led to any practical results.

During these debates Pasteur's opponents used such terms as "catalyst" or "ferment" to explain fermentations. These were said to be complex, nonliving substances which in some way aided fermentations, just as a very hot cannon ball will set fire to a pile of papers. These catalysts set off chemical reactions without entering into the reactions any more than a hot cannon ball enters into the fire which it started.

In 1897, two years after the death of Pasteur, a German chemist, Eduard Büchner, used very fine sand to grind up masses of yeast cells crushing and killing them. From this emulsion he extracted a clear fluid, which was free from all bits of yeast. When this fluid was added to sugar, alcohol was produced. Büchner showed that living yeast cells produced a substance which was not itself living, but which hastened the rate of chemical changes. Such a catalyst today is known as an *enzyme*.

In one way Pasteur's opponents had been correct. Non-living substances *do* bring about fermentations. But Pasteur was equally correct: living microbes are essential for the formation of nonliving enzymes. Büchner's experiments showed, as often happens in a controversy, that both sides of an argument may contain part of the truth.

For Pasteur's day, however, the fact that fermentation cannot occur in the absence of microbes was sufficient, and more useful than anything his opponents could offer. However revolutionary Pasteur's ideas about fermentation were 100 years ago, he did not realize that his studies would form the basis of all our understanding of how living cells keep alive, whether they are found in microbes, in plants, in animals, or in the human body. Pasteur started us on the road leading to our present understanding of the chemistry of life.

It was in 1855 when Pasteur began his work on fermentation, and little did he realize that these microbic friends of man would become an essential part of the labor force of modern industry. He could not have foreseen the large modern factories where yeasts are grown by the tons and where other microbes produce various products which man could not make without their help. Microbes help to make whiskey, wine, and beer. They flavor butter and also cheese. The scientific foundation for putting microbes to work to enrich man's life and even to protect him from disease was laid 100 years ago when Louis Pasteur guessed the nature of fermentation and proceeded to put his ideas to experimental proof.

CHAPTER 8

Where Do Microbes Come From?

THE SOLUTION of one scientific problem always raises new ones. Science grows as though men in search of truth were climbing a ladder step by step, aware that, although the top may never be reached, each step brings them nearer the truth.

The story of the work of Louis Pasteur illustrates more than that of any other single person this method of search for knowledge. He moved on and on from crystals to life, to fermentations, and then to the origin of life. This does not mean that he systematically worked on one problem, finished it, and then took up another. On the contrary, he would often return to some aspect of an old question, and for years at a time he might keep several experiments going at once.

After three years at Lille, he regretfully left to become administrator and director of scientific studies at the Ecole Normale. His alma mater needed to be reorganized, and Pasteur was ready to undertake the task. He was given two very small, ill-equipped rooms in an attic where he might do his own research. These quarters were unbearably hot in summer and miserably cold in winter. However, no matter how inadequate his working facilities were, nor how demanding his new duties might be, he would be in the great city of Paris—the center of scientific research. He was eager to go, and at the age of thirty-five, he moved his wife and three little children to Paris, which became his home and scientific headquarters for the rest of his life.

He continued his studies on fermentation, but was drawn into the age-old problem concerning the origin of life. If he were to work with microbes, understand and control their activities, he must know where they came from. Do they arise spontaneously from nonliving matter, from grape juices, from meat extracts and sugar solutions? Or do they arise from preexisting microbes?

For 2,000 years serious-minded people had wondered how life arose. Three hundred years before Christ, Aristotle had said, "Every dry body which becomes moist, and every humid body which dries up breeds life." For centuries everyone believed that life arose by spontaneous generation from nonliving things. People of the sixteenth and seventeenth centuries believed that mice arose from old rags, that frogs developed out of mud, and that insects sprang from the morning dew. However strange these notions may seem to us today, most thoughtful people believed them. From their day-to-day experiences, people associated old rags with mice and mud with frogs, and they had not learned that two events which occur together may not have any cause-and-effect relation.

It was not until the nineteenth century—the century of

Pasteur—that precision in the experimental attack in solving mysteries of nature came into full swing. Pasteur was the fighting hero of this method. In all his work, he first stated his question, thought of a way to test it, observed what happened, and then reasoned all possible conclusions which the test might suggest. If more than one conclusion appeared reasonable, then he put each to further testing, or admitted that more than one answer was possible. His genius lay in his ability to spot an important question and in his skill in creating critical experiments to test it. Often by some intuitive process he seemed to divine the answer before he had tested it, but he never accepted or fought for an idea until experiment had proved it valid.

The first person to analyze experimentally the origin of life was the Italian physician, Francesco Redi, who, in 1668, asked, "Does old meat give birth to flies?" He put meat in jars. Some he covered with cloth and others he left uncovered. The meat became putrid and the odor attracted flies. Redi watched the flies and saw them deposit their eggs on top of the cloth-covered jars, and on the meat in the uncovered jars. Flies developed only where the eggs had been laid. Since flies could not lay eggs on meat inside covered jars, Redi observed that no flies developed here. Since meat thus protected did not give rise to flies, Redi concluded that spontaneous generation did not occur. So much for flies!

About twenty years later, microbes were seen under the microscope for the first time. People who still had faith in spontaneous generation cried out—"Maybe not flies, but here in the unseen world of microbes, life arises spontaneously!" But not until about seventy years later was the question of spontaneous generation among microbes put to experimental analysis.

An Englishman named John Needham, trained as a Catholic priest, lived in Belgium. In 1748 he published the results of his experiments with meat juices. He boiled the meat and extracted the hot juices, which he put into bottles. The bottles were corked and sealed with wax. Then he heated the bottles and put them aside to cool. In time, the clear juice became cloudy and full of living microbes. Needham believed that he had killed all living forms by heat and therefore concluded that the microbes arose spontaneously from the juices.

An Italian Abbé, named Lazzaro Spallanzani, criticized Needham's tests. He thought they had not been done carefully enough because he had not stated how long nor how hot he had heated the fluid in the corked bottles. Furthermore, it was well recognized in those days, as it is today, that meat juices exposed to the air become cloudy and spoil with the growth of living microbes. It was by no means certain, argued Spallanzani, that the entrance of the air had been prevented in Needham's corked bottles.

Spallanzani set to work to support these criticisms by his own tests. He used glass flasks with long necks. Into these he put juices extracted from boiling meat, and sealed the tip of the necks airtight by passing them through a flame. He then immersed the flasks in boiling water for forty-five minutes. The liquid remained perfectly clear, and since no life developed within the juices, Spallanzani concluded that life does not arise in the microbic world by spontaneous generation.

Needham was quick to answer. Spallanzani had spoiled the "life-giving" qualities of the juices, he argued, by exposing them to the temperature of boiling water. Spallanzani responded by opening one of the flasks to the air. The life-giving properties of the juices had not been destroyed, for the juices soon became cloudy and full of microbes. Back and forth the battle raged, until gradually the idea that life did not arise spontaneously—even among microbes—became more and more generally accepted.

But the idea of spontaneous generation died hard. It was during this time that oxygen in the air was first discovered, and later that oxygen was necessary for life. Those who had faith in the idea of spontaneous generation now asked: "Had not boiling the sealed flasks so changed the oxygen within them that it could no longer support living things?" Whereupon many elaborate devices were constructed to admit filtered air into meat solutions. Again the results were confusing, for no flawless experiment could be devised.

Pasteur had been at the Ecole Normale only one year when, in 1858, scientific circles in Paris were shaken by an announcement from Félix Pouchet supporting spontaneous generation. This Frenchman, who was director of the Natural History Museum at Rouen and a member of many learned societies, addressed the Paris Academy of Sciences: "The opponents of spontaneous generation assert that the germs of microscopic organisms exist in the air, which transports them to a distance. What, then, will these opponents say if I succeed in introducing the generation of living organisms while substituting artificial air for that of the atmosphere?"

Pouchet had set up a most elaborate apparatus to meet all possible criticisms. He filled a flask with boiling water. Sealing it in a flame, he turned it upside down and thrust the neck of the bottle into a bath of mercury. He firmly clamped the bottle in this position, and when the water had cooled, he broke open the neck under mercury. Into the open neck he placed a tube from another apparatus which forced pure oxygen into the water. The pressure of the incoming oxygen pushed some of the water out, and oxygen, which is lighter than water, rose above it. When half of the water had been replaced by oxygen, Pouchet took a piece of hay which had been heated for a very long time in a very hot oven, and holding it with sterilized forceps placed it into the mouth of the bottle. The hay floated to the surface of the water and then became distributed through it.

Pouchet's experiment consisted in making a hay infusion instead of meat juice, and in using pure oxygen gas instead of air from the atmosphere. In a few days the infusion became cloudy and seething with living microbes. "Where," said Pouchet, "does life come from? It cannot come from the water which had been boiled, destroying all living germs that may have existed in it. It cannot come from the oxygen which was produced at the temperature of incandescence. It cannot have been carried in the hay, which had been heated for a long time before being introduced into the water." This life, Pouchet declared, had arisen spontaneously.

Pasteur now entered this scientific arena. Dumas and Biot urged him not to, because he would only be wasting time on experiments which would lead nowhere. They thought the whole matter was beyond the realm of scientific inquiry. Pasteur believed otherwise.

Some people accused Pasteur of entering into this scientific conflict to defend his religious convictions. Could a man as pious as Pasteur believe in the formation of life which did not support the biblical story of creation? Pouchet's conclusion went against the teachings of the bible. How unbiased could Pasteur be?

These accusations were unwarranted, for on such matters Louis Pasteur was always very clear. For him, science and religion must be kept quite separate. He once said: "When I am in my laboratory, I begin by shutting the door on materialism and on spiritualism; I observe facts alone; I seek conditions under which life manifests itself." At another time when speaking before the French Academy of Medicine he said:

In each of us there are two individuals, one the man of science who has thrown aside old notions, and who by observation, experiment and reasoning desires to obtain knowledge of nature; the other the man of feeling, of tradition, faith, or doubt; the man of sentiment who weeps at the death of his children, who cannot prove that he will see them again but believes and hopes that he will; who does not wish to die like a microbe, and says that the force within him will be transformed. The two domains within him are distinct and woe to him who wishes to make them encroach on one another in the imperfect state of human knowledge.

Pasteur went to work on the question "Where do microbes come from?" in that same thorough fashion with which he studied all problems. If he were to continue to work with microbes, and if they did arise spontaneously, it was essential for him to know the conditions that made this possible. With this degree of open-mindedness he immediately set to work to examine Pouchet's experiments.

At this time there was general agreement that the temperature of boiling water killed microbes and that nutrient fluids exposed to the air, even after they had been boiled, became "alive" with microorganisms. Therefore, did life arise in these solutions because some essential factor in the air combined with materials in the fluid, or because the air contained preexisting microbes?

Pasteur examined dust from the air. He forced air into a test tube containing a cotton plug, which filtered out suspended particles. Often the plug turned black from the material which clung to it. He soaked the plug in alcohol and ether, and under the microscope he examined the sediment which had settled to the bottom of the tube. Myriads of different kinds of microbes could be seen. Dust particles in the air did carry microbes.

He repeated Pouchet's experiment and focused a strong beam of light over the surface of the mercury bath. Dust particles suspended in the air were seen dancing in the beam of light. By patiently watching different particles, he saw them sink lower and lower and come to rest on the surface of the mercury. He spread a thick layer of dust over the mercury and slowly plunged a glass rod into it. Watching this through the beam of light, he saw the dust

Birthplace of Louis Pasteur, Dôle, France. Third door from left was entrance to his home. Small basement window just beyond opened into tannery. Pasteur was born in room directly above. His family occupied only first floor over basement

Pasteur's mother. Drawing made
by Louis when fifteen

Pasteur's father. Drawing made
by Louis when nineteen

Village of Arbois in the foothills of the Jura mountains. Boyhood
home of Pasteur

Tanning pits in basement of Pasteur's home in Dôle. These may still be seen

Pasteur as student at Ecole Normale, Paris

Microscope (magn. 500 ×) used by Pasteur in silkworm studies.

Madame Pasteur, age 31, eight years after marriage

Above: Pasteur in Strasbourg, age 30, three years after marriage

Pasteur's children, 1864. Jean-Baptiste (13); Cécile (11) holding baby, Camille; Marie-Louise (6). (Jeanne had died in 1859.)

Dr. René Dubos, New York City

Pasteur (about 45) at a villa near
Alès dictating paper on silkworm
disease to his wife

M. A. Schenk, Alès, France

Silkworm cocoons and three
emerging moths

Recently discovered etching of
the elderly Pasteur

Pasteur studying rabid rabbit
cord drying in flask

Pasteur, 1886, surrounded by children who had come to him for
vaccine treatment after being bitten by rabid dogs

Assistant in rabbit room of the
Pasteur Institute, Paris. Rabbits
were used in making anti-rabies
vaccine

The Pasteur Institute in Paris

Pasteur (aged 70) and grandson
(6), Pasteur Vallery-Radot, now a
distinguished physician in Paris

Medal presented to Pasteur on his 70th birthday during Jubilee in amphitheater at the Sorbonne

Librairie Hachette, Paris

The Jubilee. Pasteur stands by the President of the Republic. Lister greets Pasteur with outstretched arms

Librairie Hachette, Paris

form a layer around the rod and he saw the dust travel with the rod as he plunged it deeper and deeper into the mercury. Pasteur said to himself, "Pouchet undoubtedly introduced microbe-laden dust particles into the sterile water when he inserted a piece of hay. Here is a flaw."

When a globule of mercury from the laboratory bath was put into a boiled nutrient fluid, living microbes always appeared. Pasteur repeated the test in exactly the same way, except he first heated the mercury. No microbes appeared. An important flaw in Pouchet's experiment was now apparent: the hay had become contaminated with microbes which were in the mercury.

Could Pasteur work out a test that had no flaws? If so, what might such tests reveal? He proceeded slowly, using infinite care to observe every minute detail. Men who had urged him to stay out of the controversy were becoming interested. Even Dumas visited the laboratory and gave encouragement. Balard, who twenty-five years earlier had taken such personal interest in Pasteur's work with crystals, encouraged him. One of the assistants said, "All the experiments on spontaneous generation transported Balard with delight, and the laboratory became animated with his expansive joy as soon as he entered."

During one of these visits, Balard suggested using a glass flask with a long, slender, S-shaped neck—the "swanneck" flask. The history of science will never forget the contributions made by these curious little flasks.

Pasteur filled a flask half full of nutrient fluid, and heating the glass red hot, he pulled the neck of the flask out into a long, S-shaped curve. The fluid was then boiled and allowed to cool slowly. The end of the long neck was left open. Flask after flask was prepared, and flask after flask showed no growth of microbes. Today, 100 years later, some of these very same flasks containing unaltered fluid may be seen on exhibition at the Pasteur Institute in Paris. Why did these liquids fail to show living microbes?

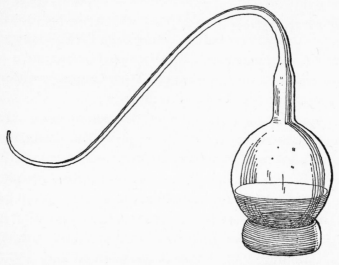

A swanneck flask

When the liquid was boiled, the escaping steam expelled the air. The flask was allowed to cool very gradually. As it did so, air from the outside moved so slowly into the neck that the microbic-laden particles were trapped within the curves. Incoming dust particles could not reach the nutrient fluid, but the untreated air could freely pass through the open neck of the flask. No one could say that the "life-supporting" qualities of the atmosphere had been destroyed.

The effect of the curves could be tested by removing

them. If a flask which had remained sterile for months was sealed in a flame and then violently shaken, in a few days its liquid became "alive" with growing microbes which had been trapped in the curve. No one could say that boiling the liquid had spoiled its life-giving properties.

After five years of the most painstaking work, Pasteur was ready to conclude that life in the world of microbes had not arisen spontaneously in the nutrient fluids of his swanneck flasks. He was ready to criticize Pouchet's experiments publicly and to report on his own. Newspapers in Paris were giving the whole controversy great publicity, public interest was reaching a high pitch, and scientists and laymen were forming into camps—the Pasteurians and the Pouchetians. For many people the whole question *was* tinged with religious feeling.

Such was the climate of opinion when a large audience composed of scientists, laymen, clergymen, writers, poets, and members of royalty filled the amphitheater of the Sorbonne on April 7, 1864 to hear Louis Pasteur speak as a scientist on spontaneous generation. He threw pictures of various microbes onto the lecture screen. These were the living forms which defenders of spontaneous generation claimed arose from nonliving matter. On the platform stood a duplicate of Pouchet's experiment, which Pasteur described as valueless because it had been performed over a mercury bath filled with dust and germs. The hall was darkened, and a beam of light fell on the surface of the mercury. Pasteur spoke:

You can see, gentlemen, the dust dancing in the luminous ray.... Look carefully at the ray of light, draw nearer to it and you will see that the little specks of dust, though moving erratically, keep sinking lower and lower.... As they float they fall. It is thus that everything becomes covered with dust, our furniture and our clothes. Thus at this moment dust is falling on all these objects, these books, these papers, this table, and on the mercury in this bath.

He described his own experiments: the collection of microbe-laden dust on a cotton filter, the fluid in the swanneck flasks which remained unchanged for months, even years. Pointing to such a fluid in a swanneck flask, he explained why it remained unchanged, and speaking slowly in a deep, low-pitched voice which carried profound conviction, he concluded:

After this, gentlemen, I can say, in showing you this liquid: I have taken from the vast universe a drop of water and filled it with nutrient jelly, that is to say, in scientific language, filled it with elements required for the development of lower organisms. I wait, I watch, I question it, and ask it kindly to reproduce for me the first creation; but it is mute. Mute during all these years since these experiments were commenced. Ah! It is because I have taken something away, taken from it in a moment the only thing which man is not gifted to produce. I have taken from it life, for life is the germ, and the germ is life. Never again will the doctrine of spontaneous generation recover from the mortal blow dealt by this simple experiment.... No! *Under no condition known today* can we affirm that microscopic beings come into the world without germs, without parents of their own nature....

His closing words were drowned by thundering applause.

The Academy of Sciences appointed a commission of experts to reexamine Pasteur's work and pronounce a final decision on spontaneous generation. Pouchet, overawed by Pasteur's confidence, withdrew. The experts, after some deliberation, issued an official report declaring a triumph for Pasteur. People considered the controversy settled once and for all. But Pasteur repeatedly affirmed that he had not proved that spontaneous generation cannot occur. He had merely made it clear that no one had ever shown that it does.

Although the doctrine of spontaneous generation has not, and may never recover from the "mortal blow" it received from Pasteur, there is a subtle error in thinking that any group of experts can sit in judgement in declaring truth. Only time can be its judge. Men can only say, as Pasteur did, "Under no conditions known today" have microbes been seen to arise spontaneously. No one can tell what observation may be made tomorrow which will cast a new light on the origin of life.

An observation *was* made a few years later which *did* show that both Pouchet and Pasteur had been working partly in the dark. It was discovered that some microbes form *spores* which resist the temperature of boiling water. These spores, or seedlike cells, survive great hardships— high temperatures, drying, and even starvation. They can wait many years for food and moisture necessary for growth and reproduction.

One kind of microbe found on grass and hay, called the "hay bacillus," does form spores. Pouchet had no doubt contaminated his piece of hay with microbes resting on the surface of the mercury, but it was also very likely that the hay itself contained spores of the "hay bacillus" which Pouchet had failed to kill. These spores were just waiting for water to moisten the hay, which then became their food.

Pasteur's nutrient broth had remained sterile only because no spores of any kind happened to be in his flasks, and because his broth happened to be made of dead yeast cells which are readily killed by boiling.

Once Pasteur became aware of the existence of microbic spores, he invented a machine—similar to the pressure cooker used in many homes—called an autoclave. With this device, solutions could be sterilized by "super-steam," which reaches a temperature many degrees above that of boiling water.

The great chemist Dumas and Biot had thought the study of spontaneous generation to be beyond the scope of scientific inquiry. But Pasteur was correct—it had to be studied, and the results obtained proved to have practical as well as theoretical value.

CHAPTER 9

Preventing Microbes from Working

LOUIS PASTEUR was a man of deep feeling and he led a tempestuous life. While serving as administrator of the Ecole Normale, he carefully watched over the comforts and health of 200 students, wrote to their parents, kept an eye on school finances, and directed the science curriculum. In addition, while working on spontaneous generation in his own small laboratory, he continued his work on fermentation and started the study of the manufacture of wine. During these first seven or eight years, he received professional honors and disappointments. His personal life was crowded with joy and sorrow. But whatever the crisis, or whatever the cause for rejoicing, work must never be neglected.

As one method of studying fermentation, he always examined the fluid under the microscope. To do this, he placed a drop of the liquid on a glass slide and covered it with a very thin piece of glass, called a cover slip. Time and time again as he studied such a preparation, he had seen microbes move toward the margin of the cover slip, where the supply of oxygen was most abundant. Suddenly on one occasion, he noticed the reverse. In a solution of butyric acid fermentation, the microbes moved away from the edge and clustered in the center of the drop. "Can it be," he asked himself, "that they are trying to escape from the oxygen of the air?"

He forced a current of air through a butyric-acid-fermenting fluid and fermentation stopped. It seemed as if the microbes were suffocating *not* from the absence of air, but from its presence. Life without air. Once again Pasteur presented an idea too revolutionary for many people to accept readily, for it had not been many years since Lavoisier, the great French chemist, had seemed to prove that oxygen in the air was essential to life.

Pasteur called microbes that needed to breathe free oxygen in the atmosphere *aerobes* and those that were inhibited or destroyed by it *anaerobes*. He reasoned out these strange phenomena by saying that the anaerobic microbes require oxygen to breathe, but that they differed from the aerobes in that they used oxygen *atoms* which are "removed from unstable compounds [substances they were using as food] instead of free oxygen gas for their respiration." In other words, as anaerobes digested their food, oxygen *atoms* were set free which they could use. Most curiously, they could not use free, atmospheric oxygen gas, which occurs in the form of molecules of oxygen—two atoms of oxygen forming one molecule.

Just before going to the Ecole Normale, Pasteur had, at the insistence of Dumas, Balard, and Biot, presented himself as a candidate for admission to the Academy of Sciences. This society of distinguished scientists elected a

new member to take the place left by the death of one of
them. Pasteur needed thirty votes to be elected. He
thought he might receive twenty, but only sixteen were
cast in his favor. He had expected defeat, but it hurt when
it came.

Three years later, in 1861, an opening appeared in the
botanical section of the Academy. Again his friends urged
his election. Biot, the oldest member of the Academy,
longed to see Louis installed as one of his colleagues. But
the question was raised: "Is Pasteur really a botanist? He
has only shown chemical changes which microscopic plants
[microbes] can bring about!" Again he failed to be
elected, receiving only twenty-four votes. However, by
December of the following year, he was admitted to the
section of mineralogy with a vote of thirty-six out of a possible sixty.

Biot had died only a few months earlier in his ninetieth
year, so that he never lived to see his last wish realized—to
see Louis Pasteur a member of the Academy of Sciences in
Paris. Nor did Biot live to hear Pasteur two years later
give his famous speech on spontaneous generation at the
Sorbonne—a study which Biot had at first tried to dissuade
Pasteur from undertaking.

Early in the morning following Pasteur's election to the
Academy, Mme. Pasteur went to Biot's grave with flowers.
She placed them there in memory of the man whom she
had come to love, the man who had advised and befriended
Louis since their first meeting to discuss right- and left-
hand crystals. A few years before his death, Biot had given
Louis a photograph of himself saying, "If you place this

near a portrait of your father, you will unite the pictures of two men who have loved you very much in the same way." Indeed, the friendship between this elderly scientist and the younger man was one of the finest to be found in the history of science.

Pasteur had been in Paris only a year, absorbed in reorganizing the Ecole, when his fourth child was born, another little girl named Marie-Louise. Five years later his fifth and last child, Camille arrived, in July of 1863. But these joys were mixed with sorrow, for when Marie-Louise was only a year old, his eldest daughter, Jeanne, at the age of nine developed typhoid fever while visiting her grandfather in Arbois. Mme. Pasteur left at once to be with Jeanne, but Pasteur was obliged to remain in Paris to complete the examination of students who were candidates for the agrégation.

Letters between the parents passed almost daily. Little Jeanne grew increasingly weak. Pasteur's letters always expressed conviction that his daughter would recover, and Mme. Pasteur tried to spare him as much anxiety as possible. But the strain was very great. As hope for her recovery began to fade, Pasteur tenderly wrote:

Paris, 8 September, 1859.

My dear Marie,

... I wish that after your return there could be nothing between us and with us but our love, our children, their education and their future with my dreams as a scientist. For you and for them a little enriched by my work, the success of new discoveries and warmest emotions. Oh! how I would regret to die without having given you all that.

Jeanne grew worse, and Pasteur rushed to Arbois, only to witness her death. Immediately after, he wrote to tell Jean-Baptiste, only a year younger than Jeanne, that his sister had just died, and that he and his mother would return to Paris at once to be with him and Cécile and baby Marie-Louise.

Pasteur had known before what it meant to lose a dear one—he had lost his mother and his sister—but this was the first time he had lost one of his children. He tried to bury himself in work, but his mind was always on little Jeanne. Three months later, he found it impossible to write a New Year's greeting to his father that carried any comfort:

It is with great sadness that I take my pen to wish you a good year for 1860. I cannot keep my thoughts from my poor little girl, so good, so happy in her little life, whom this fatal year now ending has taken away from us. She was growing to be such a comfort to her mother and to me, and to us all. . . . But forgive me, dearest father, for recalling these sad memories. She is happy; let us think of those who remain and try as much as lies within our power to keep from them the bitterness of this life.

What irony that the man who discovered that vaccines can be made should have lost his own child before anyone had learned how to make a vaccine against typhoid fever.

But Pasteur must work, and work he did. Studies on fermentation of beet juice in the manufacture of alcohol raised questions on the alcoholic fermentation of grape juice to make wine. France was exporting less and less wine because it spoiled and turned sour, or became bitter, or "ropy." These changes were known as "diseases" of wine.

Pasteur knew good wine. Had he not been raised on the best that comes from France—the red and white wines from the vineyards in the valley of the Jura mountains. His country needed his help, and he was perhaps the man who could restore the wine industry to France. He asked for nothing more than to serve his country.

For generations, wine makers had picked the ripe, sweet grapes in late September, crushed them in wooden presses, and stored them in vats over the winter. As grape sugar changed to carbon dioxide and alcohol, the juices fermented. With the introduction of alcohol, grape juice became wine. But this was new, young wine. It was cloudy, thick, opaque and had a raw taste. It must "age" and must become transparent, develop a "bouquet," or fragrance, and acquire a delicious flavor.

The older the wine, the more perfect it became, but too often the very process of aging spoiled it. Pasteur set about to study the chemistry of fermentation, of aging, and of spoiling. Only by understanding every step in making wine could he hope to discover methods of controlling the final product.

The microscope was his ally. He examined drops of healthy wine, of sour, bitter, and ropy wine. Under the microscope he looked at them over and over again. In "healthy" wine he saw only yeast cells. In "diseased" wines, there were always large numbers of other kinds of microbes. Sour wine always had one kind, bitter wine another, and ropy wine still another. He became so familiar with these microscopic findings that he was able to predict how a wine would taste by merely seeing a drop of it under the microscope. It was clear that these unwanted microbes must be controlled. If possible, they must be killed.

Pasteur proved that when sweet, ripe grapes are picked, they are covered with wild yeast cells which drop on them from the air. These yeasts work on the grape sugar first and cause fermentation. If disease microbes are present when the wine is bottled and set aside to age, it is then that these unwanted microbes begin their work. Depending upon which type of microbe happens to enter, wine becomes sour, ropy, or bitter. How could these undesirable microbes be destroyed?

Objectionable microbes were introduced into the wine from the hands of the pickers and from contaminated presses or vats. "It would be far easier to destroy them after the grape juice had fermented than to try to prevent their entrance," reasoned Pasteur. But first he must understand the chemistry of the aging process.

Practical wine makers believed that too much **exposure** to the oxygen of the air spoiled the flavor of wine as it aged. Therefore they took great precaution when they bottled the wine to prevent it from coming in contact with the air. Pasteur asked himself, "What is the relation of oxygen in the air to the aging of wine?"

By simple experiments, he discovered the answer to be somewhat complex. He filled a bottle to the brim with new, young wine, corked it and sealed it with wax. Under these conditions, with the amount of air reduced to minimum, it never aged. It remained thick, opaque, and still tasted raw.

He next filled a bottle only half full of young wine, thus admitting considerable air. He sealed it with a cork which he did not wax, thus providing a continuous entrance of air and oxygen from the outside. Under these conditions, and in the absence of any disease microbes, the wine became clear, transparent, and developed a pleasing bouquet and a delicious flavor. If too much air was present, however, the color faded and the flavor vanished. It was evident, therefore, that oxygen aided in the aging, provided there was not too much of it.

It then became clear that it was necessary actually to kill undesirable microbes that might be present before the wine was set aside in bottles or casks to age. The citizens of Arbois, where Pasteur always spent his summer vacation, offered their help. The wines of the Jura too often became sour. Pasteur could help them, and they offered to give him a makeshift laboratory where he could work during the summer. The town would pay all expenses. In 1864 Pasteur wrote to the mayor and the town council: "This spontaneous offer from a town dear to me for so many reasons does too much honor to my modest labors, and the way in which it is made covers me with confusion."

He refused financial aid from the town for fear that he might not succeed, and instead set himself up in an old café close to his father's house. There was no gas in the improvised laboratory, and the only source of heat for his experiments came from a charcoal fire which burned in an old metal pan. Duclaux, his assistant at the Ecole Normale, came with him. Together they kept the fire burning by fanning it from time to time with a pair of bellows. They washed laboratory instruments and dishes in the Cuisance River, which also supplied the water which they carried to the laboratory. For tables they used old boards supported on blocks of timber. And it was in these most primitive quarters that the theory and practice of *pasteurization* was developed.

At one time Pasteur had tried to destroy the unwanted microbes, and thus prevent them from doing their mischief, by using various antiseptics. But to use enough of these chemicals to bring death to the microbes, brought an undesirable flavor to the wine. He decided to try to kill them by heat. What was the lowest temperature that he could use and be certain that they were dead?

After many trials, he discovered that if wine was kept at a temperature of 55° centigrade (water boils at 100° centigrade) for several minutes, all "disease-producing" microbes that might be present were killed. Here was the answer. If young wine is heated in bottles or casks in the presence of a small amount of air, it will age and never spoil. It was this heating process which later became known as *pasteurization*.

Wine making, which could now be carried on as a science as well as an art, consisted first in permitting yeasts to cause fermentation, and later in preventing undesirable microbes from working by killing them with heat. Oxygen and time did the aging.

It would seem reasonable to suppose that now the problem was solved. But, no! Pasteur had to fight prejudice, because people complained that "cooked" wine tasted strange. True, it was neither sour, nor bitter, nor ropy, but they claimed the bouquet had been altered and that different wines had lost their distinctive flavors.

Pasteur was not a professional winetaster, but he knew good wine when he drank it. He could not detect any change in the taste of pasteurized wine. But such a statement carried little weight. Furthermore, he wanted to test this matter of taste as scientifically as possible.

There was only one way to do this: he employed the services of a group of professional winetasters. They spent a week tasting twenty-one wines of different ages gathered from various regions of France. Some of the samples were heated and other samples of the same wine were not. Nine times out of ten these experts failed to detect any difference between heated and unheated samples. Pasteur went so far as to indulge in pranks to show what tricks the imagination could play in matters regarding taste. He merely divided the contents of one bottle of wine into two samples, and asked the experts whether they could detect any difference without revealing to them the source of the samples. They *all* claimed they could taste a difference.

Pasteur had made his discovery, but he still had to sell its value to wine makers and to the people of France. Fortunately, in all of his work he seemed as eager to have one of his discoveries accepted and made useful to mankind as he was in making the discovery.

For several years he worked to spread news of the importance of pasteurization in preserving wine, beer, milk, and other food products. He wrote popular newspaper articles explaining the method and discussing its value. He consulted with wine makers to make sure they used the method correctly. For engineers, he drew diagrams of an apparatus that could be used to heat large quantities of wine at one time. He paid careful attention to the cost of such operations in order to make it cheap and practical. He was determined that France should benefit from his discovery of preserving wine.

In the midst of these discussions, Dumas suddenly asked Pasteur to undertake another problem. It would mean that Louis would have to leave his laboratory at the Ecole for perhaps several years. How could he ever make such a sacrifice? Yet how could he possibly refuse a request from Dumas, who had been one of his greatest teachers and to whom he owed so much?

CHAPTER 10

Saving the Silk Industry for France

IT WAS in the spring of 1865 that Pasteur entered his laboratory and called out to his assistant, Duclaux, "Do you know what Professor Dumas has just asked me to do? Go to the south and study a disease in silkworms!"

"Is there such a disease?" asked Duclaux.

"I didn't know it, but there must be. I've never even touched a silkworm," lamented Pasteur.

The French Senate had just received a petition signed by over three thousand mayors, councilmen, and landowners in silk-producing regions of southern France. They called upon the government to undertake research on a disease among silkworms which was reducing the earnings of many peasants and seriously threatening the economy of France.

Since 1845 these epidemics had spread from country to country. They had invaded Italy, Spain, Greece, Turkey, and even China. By 1864 the only healthy silkworm eggs came from Japan, and many Frenchmen had long since given up hope of raising their own eggs. Even those from Japan could not always be counted on.

The silkworm industry was very seasonal—lasting only

two months—but during these weeks of hard work the peasants had been able to increase their earnings by raising silkworms and selling the silky cocoons. Where prosperity had once prevailed, now there was only misery. As Dumas wrote to Pasteur: "The distress is beyond anything you can imagine."

Dumas, a native of southern France, was a senator from Le Gard—a province where the town of Alès is an important silkworm center. In despair, he turned to Pasteur, hoping that Louis might help these desperate people and save the industry, not only for France but for other countries in Europe and Asia. When Pasteur made it clear to Dumas that he knew nothing about silkworms, much less their diseases, Dumas replied: "So much the better. For ideas, you will have only those which shall come to you as a result of your own observations."

What a new experience for Pasteur. In his previous work he had always had some hunch before attacking a problem and would proceed to devise experiments to test it. In working with crystals he had thought that there *must* be some difference between tartaric and paratartaric acid, and he hunted until he found it. He had believed that fermentations were caused by microbes and proceeded to devise a series of tests to prove it. In his work on spontaneous generation he had believed that dust particles in the air probably carried microbes, and it did not take him long to demonstrate the truth of this hunch. Now, for the first time, he would have to let some observation give him his initial hypothesis, then test it, evaluate it, and proceed step by step.

The more Pasteur thought about the silkworm problem, the more he wanted to study it, even though it would take him away from his laboratory at the Ecole Normale. He had discovered that the so-called "diseases" of wines were caused by microbes. Might the silkworm disease be due to some parasite?

On June 6, 1865, he left Paris for Alès, 500 miles to the south. Before leaving he read about the history of the silkworm industry, which dated back some 4,000 years. He learned something about the biology of the strange little creatures on which the industry depended and discovered that several scientists had already studied a disease in silkworms called *pébrine*. Microscopic examination of the tissues of these sickly worms showed tiny particles which had been called "corpuscles." Were these corpuscles the cause of pébrine? No one knew. Pasteur had no hunches, but he intended to understand and control the disease if he could.

The life history of the silkworm is long and complicated. The species used in France is known as an *annual*. That is, the adult female moth lays her eggs in late May or June, and the tiny silkworms do not hatch from these eggs until the following spring.

When April comes, the worms emerge from the eggs and at once begin feeding on mulberry leaves. During the next thirty-five days, they grow to be large, fat, yellowish worms more than 1½ inches long. During this time they cast off their skin four times, that is, they have four *molts*. Although the worms consume more and more mulberry leaves as they grow older, during their last molt they eat ravenously. They never stop chewing, and the continuous grinding of their little jaws make a noise that Pasteur compared to the sound of rain beating against trees during a storm. At the end of this *grande gorge,* silence begins to fall, the worms stop eating, raise their heads, and restlessly search about for something to climb upon where they can rest and quietly spin their silky cocoons.

This house of silk that a worm spins over and around itself protects it during the next two weeks, while it goes through two more changes inside its cocoon—first to the pupa, then to the moth, or butterfly. The pupa, which is covered by a hard, brownish shell, soon transforms into the moth. As the moth emerges from its cocoon, it breaks many silky threads trying to escape.

Although the moths have wings, they never fly, for their sole function is reproduction. After mating, the female lays a batch of eggs—500 or more. Worms which develop from the same batch are called a *brood,* or a *culture.* After the eggs begin to hatch, it takes about two months for the worms to develop into egg-laying moths.

Silkworm growers raise the worms in a nursery which the French call a *magnanerie.* In such a building, the worms grow and molt in trays which fit on shelves built one above another. Workers in a magnanerie are in constant attendance. They keep the worms well supplied with freshly picked mulberry leaves, they clean the trays, and day by day anxiously watch the worms' growth and behavior.

After the grande gorge, when the worms have ceased to eat, the commercial grower places twigs in the trays for the

worms to climb upon to spin their cocoons.   If he wishes
to sell the cocoons for silk, he does not allow the moths to
emerge, because the broken threads spoil the silk for com-

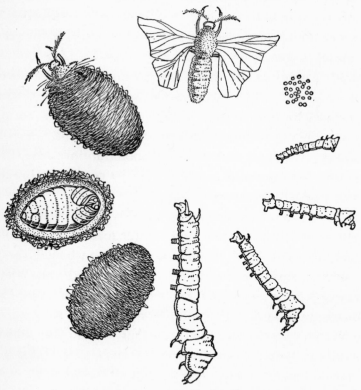

Life cycle of a silkworm

mercial use.   Therefore, five or six days after the worms
have ascended the twigs and finished spinning their cocoons, the grower harvests the cocoons and places them in
a steam bath.   This kills the imprisoned pupae but does
not spoil the silk.

When silk is manufactured, the cocoon is steamed to soften a gummy substance that covers each fiber. The cocoon is then unwound, and several strands of its delicate fibers are reeled together to make a single thread of silk.

If the commercial grower wishes to obtain eggs which he can sell or use himself, he allows the moths to emerge normally, and provides trays upon which they lay their eggs. These tiny eggs, which are about the size of the head of a pin, are kept through the winter in boxes perforated to allow plenty of air.

In 1865 no such healthy picture could be seen in any magnanerie in all of France. In Alès, Pasteur saw sick worms covered with black specks as though they had been sprinkled with pepper. Hence the disease had been called pébrine, from the peasant word *pébré,* meaning pepper. Sometimes the worms died before they could even begin spinning, or if they did spin, the cocoons were poor.

Pasteur talked with the peasants, many of whom raised silkworms in their homes, to learn all he could from their experiences, hoping that their stories might suggest some scientific explanation which he might test. He found nothing but superstition. Some workers sprayed the mulberry leaves with wine or rum, some fumigated the magnanerie with chlorine or coal tar, while others preferred to sprinkle sulfur powder on the worms. Year after year the cultures failed—nothing helped.

These contradictory stories gave him no clue, and he settled in a small magnanerie near Alès where two broods, or cultures, of worms were being cultivated. The eggs of both cultures had come from Japan. One of them was progressing well with the production of fine cocoons, while the worms in the other culture were sick and would not eat. At once Pasteur had an idea. He would make a comparative study of these two cultures, an apparently healthy one and one that was obviously sick. The microscope might show something that would give him his first hypothesis.

He had been in Alès only nine days when word came that Jean-Joseph was very ill. Pasteur left everything and started for Arbois—250 miles to the north. On the long, slow journey, he was filled with foreboding for he kept thinking of the time when he had left Paris at news of his mother's illness. Would he again arrive too late? He thought of little Jeanne who had died in Arbois six years earlier while visiting her grandfather. The journey seemed endless. Arriving at the station at Arbois, he was met by some cousins dressed in deep black, and at once he knew he was too late. He arrived only in time to attend the ceremony at the grave. Late that night in a silent room upstairs in the old tannery, he wrote to his family in Paris:

My dear Marie, my dear children,
Dear grandfather is no more; we have taken him this morning to his last resting place, close to little Jeanne's. Until the last moment I hoped I should see him again, embrace him for the last time.... I have been thinking all day of the marks of affection I had from my father. For thirty years I have been his constant care, I owe everything to him. When I was young he kept me from bad company and instilled into me the habit of working and the example of the most loyal and best-filled life.... You did not know him, dearest Marie, at the time when he and my mother were working so hard for the children they loved, for me

especially, whose books and schooling cost so much.... We shall talk often of dear grandfather.... I long to see you all, but must go back to Alais [Alès], for my studies would be retarded by a year if I could not spend a few days there now.

Louis Pasteur was soon back in Alès intent upon discovering what his microscope might show. His ability to concentrate when there was work to do had helped him before in times of grief. It came to his rescue now.

To his complete surprise, he found that pupae and moths from the healthy culture were filled with corpuscles, whereas there were none in the sickly brood. But as the sickly worms developed into pupae and then to moths, corpuscles appeared in increasing numbers. Finally, all moths from the sick culture showed corpuscles. Confusing as this seemed, Pasteur formulated his first hypotheses. These were his hunches:

1. Pébrine is a disease inherent in the animal, that is, it is constitutional. It is *not* caused by the corpuscles.

2. Corpuscles represent broken-down tissue, and their presence can be used as an indication of the extent of the disease.

3. Moths with corpuscles will produce eggs that carry the disease. Only those moths free from corpuscles will lay healthy eggs. Therefore, the breeder must make microscopic studies of all egg-laying moths.

On the basis of these hunches, he made the following recommendations for the selection of healthy eggs:

1. Isolate each couple (male and female) just before mating.

2. After egg laying, microscopically examine each parent for corpuscles by crushing the moth and mixing the material in a drop of liquid. If corpuscles are absent in both male and female, this batch of eggs should produce a healthy culture.

These were only hypotheses and must be tested. Pasteur set about to find corpuscular and noncorpuscular moths for comparative study. He had no problem in finding corpuscular ones—they were everywhere, but he had to examine hundreds of couples to find only three noncorpuscular pairs. He carefully labeled eggs from these different matings, and set them aside for cultivation the following year.

He went back to Paris to resume his duties at the Ecole Normale, only to face another personal bereavement: his two-year-old Camille became very ill. He spent his days at the Ecole, and at night he sat by the bed of his dying baby. In September he wrote to Dumas: "My poor child died this morning, always remaining so clear in her mind that when her little hands became cold, she kept asking me to put them into mine, something she had never done during her long illness, and until her last breath, she spoke with her usual intelligence to those around her."

Pasteur took the tiny coffin to Arbois where so many of those he loved were now buried.

Back in Paris, he started to write an article on the life and work of Lavoisier—another task which Dumas had assigned him. Antoine Lavoisier was a French chemist who lost his life at the guillotine in 1792, during the French

Revolution. Although this great scientist had been killed at the prime of life, his contributions to chemistry were remarkable. He introduced precision into chemical studies by measuring the exact amount of carbon dioxide and alcohol obtained from a known amount of sugar, although he never dreamed that yeast cells did the fermenting. He demonstrated that oxygen was essential to life.

Pasteur was filled with enthusiasm as he read of Lavoisier's logic in reasoning, of his patience while observing nature, and of his ability to rise above many burdens. He wrote of him: ". . . Though chemical and physical knowledge accumulated since his time has gone beyond all Lavoisier's dreams, his work, like that of Newton and a few other rare spirits, will remain ever young. Certain details will age, . . . but the foundation, the method constitute one of the great aspects of the human mind, the majesty of which is only increased by years." Reading the lives of great men always inspired Pasteur, and it was good for him to become absorbed in writing about one of them just at a time when his own personal problems so weighed upon him.

Pasteur again left Paris early in February for Alès, eager to cultivate the two sets of eggs which he had selected the previous year. Would his predictions hold true? He settled in a large, comfortable house at the foot of the mountains about a mile from Alès. Two assistants came with him, and Duclaux joined them later. In May, Mme. Pasteur planned to come with their two daughters, Cécile and Marie-Louise.

In April, after the two daughters had finished their term

at school, they started with their mother for Alès, stopping first for a short visit with grandmother Laurent in Chambéry. No sooner had they arrived than Cécile, who was twelve years old, became ill with typhoid fever. The courageous mother did not ask her husband to leave his work and go to Chambéry, but her letters so alarmed him, that he left at once and stayed with them for two weeks.

The crisis seemed over, and Pasteur went back to Alès. Several days later, Cécile suffered a relapse and died. Just before her death—almost as though he anticipated it—Pasteur gave way to despondency and wrote to his wife in desperation: "Our beloved children die one after another. I long to join you, my dear children. . . . I wish so much to be close to you, close to you, my dear Cécile. Oh! if you can stay, stay with us."

Mme. Pasteur was torn between returning to Paris to be with her son, Jean-Baptiste, who was still in school, or going to Alès to be with her husband. She finally wrote to her son: "I could not leave your poor father to go back to Alais [Alès] alone after this great sorrow."

Pasteur's wife, who was his greatest comfort and always gave him courage, went with him and with Marie-Louise to Alès. Duclaux joined them and everyone, including Mme. Pasteur and Marie-Louise, set to work on the silk-worm study. They collected mulberry leaves from trees growing on the mountainside, they helped in raising the worms and in the collection and selection of the eggs. Even Marie-Louise learned to detect corpuscles through the microscope. It was a congenial, hard-working little party. Pasteur had never struggled more with personal grief, nor had he ever been happier in his research. The study of pébrine was getting more interesting every day.

Pasteur's predictions about the batches of eggs all came true. Eggs from corpuscular moths hatched sickly cultures, and eggs from noncorpuscular moths hatched healthy ones. He was making good progress, but how should he interpret what he found? His assistants had come to the conclusion that corpuscles *were* the cause of pébrine, because in one experiment healthy worms fed debris from corpuscular worms grew sick and produced only a few cocoons. The moths from this culture finally became full of corpuscles.

His assistants were therefore surprised when later Pasteur still reported that corpuscles were *not* the cause of pébrine. His reasons can be stated as follows:

1. In many instances the disease appeared before corpuscles could be seen.

2. Feeding worms corpuscular material killed the worms rapidly without giving them corpuscles.

3. No method of reproduction of the corpuscles could be discovered.

From these facts, the evidence did not seem to point to corpuscles as the culprits. But Pasteur was handicapped because he had never studied protozoa—animal microbes. He had only seen plant microbes: yeast cells that multiply by budding and bacteria that reproduce by splitting. The corpuscles of pébrine were protozoa that invade tissues of the worms, of the pupae, and of the moths. They multiply while inside these cells, and during this time they are difficult to observe. After multiplying, they burst from the cells and become visible again in the body fluid.

The silkworm season of the next year opened with great disappointments but closed with new discoveries. Pasteur had distributed many batches of healthy eggs to various commercial breeders. Some of these developed successfully, but many failed. As more and more letters reporting failure came pouring in, Pasteur became absorbed and hardly spoke to his assistants. The fact was that he, too, was meeting failure in the cultivation of his own eggs. Out of sixteen broods, fifteen developed well, while the sixteenth was a complete failure.

All failures showed exactly the same well-defined pattern: the disease attacked *all the worms at exactly the same time*. This was a new picture, for pébrine did not behave this way. Suddenly an explanation flashed across Pasteur's mind, and in despair he went to his assistants. Almost in tears, he dropped into a chair and lamented, "Nothing is accomplished. There are *two* diseases."

His assistants tried to encourage him. They reminded him that he had found the method of controlling pébrine. Now they would all go to work to solve this other disease, which was obviously the one that previous workers had called *flacherie,* or *flaccid death*. In time, Pasteur discovered that the intestine of a healthy worm was almost free from any microbes, whereas the intestine of a worm with flacherie was swarming with them. Eggs from moths with flacherie carried the infection.

The presence of flacherie could easily be told by the sluggish behavior of the worm as it climbed the twig, even though it might spin an excellent cocoon. But moths of such worms would lay infected eggs, and the disease would break out in worms of the next generation. The disease was sometimes serious enough to cause the death of the worms before spinning. Moths suffering from flacherie should never be used for egg laying.

Now that the two diseases had been distinguished, Pasteur turned once more to the question of the role of corpuscles in pébrine. He injected corpuscles into worms developing from the eggs of noncorpuscular moths. Corpuscles appeared, the worms grew sick and soon showed all the signs of pébrine. From these observations there was now only one conclusion, and Pasteur was quick to revise his earlier opinion, stating that the corpuscles are the cause, and the *only* cause of pébrine. Now he could explain why those other worms fed on corpuscular material died without showing corpuscles: they had doubtlessly succumbed to flacherie.

The silkworm project was near solution, and Pasteur proceeded to recommend methods of egg selection:

1. Examine microscopically all moths used for egg laying. Burn all eggs from corpuscular moths. Use only eggs from noncorpuscular parents. Only such eggs will be free from pébrine.

2. If worms climb the twig in a languishing manner, never allow these worms to develop moths for egg laying, no matter how good their cocoons may be. Such eggs will be infected with flacherie microbes.

These theories would have to be rigorously tested the following year, but Pasteur felt confident that the conquest of the silkworm diseases was close at hand.

While in Alès, Pasteur had received word that in Paris on July 1 the grand prize medal of the 1867 exhibition would be conferred upon him for his work on wines. He wrote to Dumas expressing his surprise and gratitude for this honor, for he believed that his old master had undoubtedly submitted his name to the Emperor—Napoleon III. Pasteur's return to Paris this year was thus filled with special excitement.

On the appointed day Paris was a gay and colorful spectacle. The boulevards were lined with regiments of infantry, dragoons, and imperial guards as the Emperor and Empress Eugenie passed in their imperial carriage drawn by eight horses. Then followed a procession of foreign nobility: the Crown Prince of Wales, Prince Humbert of Italy, the Duke and Duchess of Aosta, and the Grand Duchess Marie of Russia. The procession entered the Palais de l'Industrie and mounted the stage before an excited audience of 17,000 spectators.

The impressive ceremony opened with a speech from the Emperor, who expressed his hopes of peace and prosperity. Then came the conferring of the grand prizes. As each candidate's name was called, he mounted the stage and was presented to the Emperor by Marshall Valliant, minister of the Emperor's household. The Emperor himself then handed the medal to the recipient. Many names well known to the audience, such as Ferdinand de Lesseps, who was honored for his engineering success in building the Suez Canal, brought forth great applause.

The name Louis Pasteur was called. A middle-aged man, rather short and stocky, with jet-black hair and a

close-trimmed beard walked forward with simple dignity.
The applause was slight, for his scientific discoveries leading to his work on wines were then known to only a few.
An eyewitness wrote: "I was struck with his simplicity and
gravity; the seriousness of his life was visible in his stern,
almost sad eyes." Only a very few in that audience could
possibly have predicted that in later years his own coun-
trymen would by popular vote elect Louis Pasteur as the
greatest son of France.

Just at this time, the Ecole Normale Supérieure was in
a political upheaval. Over one hundred inhabitants of St.
Etienne had presented a petition to the Senate protesting
against the presence of certain books in their public library. The volumes they wished banned as politically or
morally dangerous included the writings of several great
French authors: Rousseau, Voltaire, Balzac, and George
Sand. The vote of the Senate in support of the petition
infuriated one Senator, Sainte-Beuve, who gave a vigorous
speech in support of freedom of thought. Sainte-Beuve
called the Senate decision scandalous.

The students of the Ecole were stirred by the liberal at-
titude expressed by the courageous Senator, and one of
them, named Lallier, wrote to him expressing the gratitude of them all for his defense of freedom of speech. This
letter, which was printed in a newspaper of Paris, stirred
public opinion to a high pitch.

Nicard, who was director of the Ecole Normale, expelled
Lallier in support of a government ruling which forbade
any political demonstration by students. Pasteur, who was
politically naive and always a defender of authority and

discipline, gave his full support to Nicard. The students rebelled and demanded that Lallier be allowed to return immediately. Pasteur tried in vain to pacify them, and while talking to them, they rose in a body, left the school and paraded the streets of Paris. In the face of such disorder, the government temporarily closed the Ecole. When it reopened a few months later, three great chiefs were all relieved of their posts: Nicard, the director, Pasteur, administrator and director of scientific studies, and Jacquinet, director of literary studies.

Pasteur's students in the scientific division were shocked at this unexpected outcome, and one of them wrote to him that if it were yet possible to prevent his departure, "all students at the Ecole will be only too happy to do everything in their power. . . . As for me, it is impossible to express my gratitude toward you. No one has ever shown me so much interest, and never in my life shall I forget what you have done for me."

Duruy, Minister of Public Education, supported Pasteur, but all efforts to reinstate him were made in vain. The government had spoken. The experience, however, proved to be no personal calamity for Pasteur. His connection with the Ecole was retained when a post was created for him as director of a new department, that of physiological chemistry (the chemistry of living processes). In addition he was made professor of organic chemistry at the Sorbonne. Now he would lecture in the same room where, twenty-five years earlier as a student, he had been so inspired by the lectures of Dumas.

For some time Pasteur had been greatly concerned over the failure of the French government to give sufficient financial support to scientific research. France had once been the intellectual leader among European nations, but he now saw his country falling far behind. In 1865 he had written to Napoleon III asking for larger laboratories and better equipment to extend his work on microorganisms, which had opened new vistas in medicine. Without adequate facilities for housing experimental animals, without spacious, well-equipped laboratories, it would be impossible to carry on the experiments he now planned. Napoleon was sympathetic to his request and agreed to erect new buildings in the garden of the Ecole Normale. However, two years passed and government support was not forthcoming.

Undaunted, Pasteur continued his campaign. He wrote an appeal which he planned to have printed in a Paris newspaper so that all public authorities would be made aware of the deplorable conditions under which French scientists were forced to work. After making a passionate plea for more laboratories which are "temples of the future, of riches and of comfort," he compared the handicaps imposed upon French scientists to those of other countries. "Some nations have felt the wholesome breath of truth. Rich and large laboratories have been growing in Germany for the last thirty years, and many more are still being built; at Berlin and at Bonn two palaces, worth 4 million francs each, are being erected for chemical studies. St. Petersburg has spent 3½ million francs on a physiological institute; England, America, Austria, Bavaria have made generous sacrifices. Italy too has made a start. And France? France has not yet begun. . . ."

Although the article was refused publication in the *Moniteur*, it reached Napoleon, who read it with sympathetic understanding. Later the Emperor called a private meeting with Pasteur and three other scientists. At this meeting further details were discussed whereby not only a new laboratory would be erected at the Ecole Normale, but new emphasis would be given to the training of future scientists. They left, confident that Napoleon intended to promote their cause.

In March of that year Pasteur left for Alès—the very day that Napoleon announced his decision to make improvements in Pasteur's laboratory. And, Duruy, Minister of Public Education, now felt assured that French scientists would soon be given equipment to match that of their German colleagues across the Rhine.

Arriving at Alès, Pasteur found that silkworm breeders who had carefully followed his directions for detecting pébrine had met with complete success. Those who had disregarded his recommendations had failed. The control of flacherie was difficult, however, for it was now evident that many factors influenced its appearance, such as feeding rotting mulberry leaves to the silkworms, or sudden storms, or changes in temperature. Any one of these factors lowered the resistance of some worms to the intestinal microbes of flacherie. In order to obtain eggs free from flacherie microbes, Pasteur recommended that scrapings of the digestive tract of egg-laying moths be mixed with water and examined under the microscope. The flacherie microbes could be easily detected.

It now appeared that the diseases of silkworms could be controlled by microscopic examination of moths, by feeding the worms dry mulberry leaves, by observing the behavior of worms as they climbed the twigs to spin their cocoons, and by keeping culture trays immaculately clean and the nurseries well ventilated and at a constant temperature.

These precautions challenged old practices of silkworm merchants, and some of them saw their industry jeopardized. Some claimed that the microscope was made for scientists and that it was nonsense to expect peasants to use it. In answer to such fears, Pasteur had two years earlier shown them his eight-year-old daughter, Marie-Louise, sitting in his laboratory looking through a microscope. If she had learned to detect corpuscles, they could.

A false rumor had spread to Lyon that Pasteur's failures had so infuriated the people of Alès that he had been forced to flee the city to escape being stoned by the mobs. But Pasteur had fought jealousy and prejudice before, and he would conquer his adversaries now. He took courage from the fact that ten microscopes were being used in various parts of Alès to insure the production of healthy eggs. He was prepared to fight any necessary battle to save the silk industry for France.

Back in Paris, he was full of plans for the building of the new laboratory, which was now assured, since 30,000 francs had been granted by the Minister of Public Instruction and an equal amount by the Minister of the Emperor's

household. He looked forward to his classes at the Sorbonne, which would take every spare moment of his time.
To add to his satisfactions, the University of Bonn had
granted him the honorary degree of doctor of medicine, in
recognition of his work with microbes. The German system, which he so admired, had indeed paid him great
homage.

Absorbed with life full to overflowing, he threw himself
into his work with great enthusiasm. He could not know
that terrible days were just ahead.

CHAPTER 11

Crises in Mid-career

OCTOBER 19, 1868 always remained a bitter date in the memory of Pasteur's family and friends. That day, in spite of a severe chill which forced him to lie down after lunch, he insisted upon going to the Academy of Sciences. He was scheduled to read a communication from an Italian silkgrower who had successfully followed Pasteur's recommendations for breeding healthy worms.

Mme. Pasteur, concerned for his health, invented an errand in order to walk with him to the Academy. Meeting Professor Balard on her return, she said: "I am anxious about Louis. He suffered a severe chill this noon, and I beg of you to see that he returns home safely."

Pasteur read the report in his characteristic slow, steady voice and remained until the end of the meeting. Balard and Sainte Claire Deville walked home with him. Usually Mme. Pasteur read aloud to him after dinner, but that night he went to bed early. He suffered another attack. He could not speak and his left leg and arm became too heavy to move. Finally speech returned, and he was able to call for help. Mme. Pasteur at once summoned his close friend Dr. Godelier, but Pasteur had no illusions. He knew that he had had a paralytic stroke.

Consultation with two other physicians was immediately called, and bloodletting was recommended. Sixteen leeches were placed behind the ears and the blood flowed profusely. For twenty-four hours his life hung in the balance. Official bulletins were issued:

> October 20, 10 P.M.: Speech clearer, some movement of paralyzed limb; intelligence perfect.
> 2 A.M.: Intense cold, anxious agitation, features depressed, eyes languid.

Mme. Pasteur, usually so gay and courageous, feared for his life. Moments of despair alternated with those of renewed hope.

> October 21, 2:30 P.M.: Mind active, would willingly talk science.

Colleagues hastened to Pasteur's home—an apartment in the Ecole Normale—and begged to help Mme. Pasteur and Dr. Godelier. Professor Sainte Claire Deville, the first to arrive, stood by the bedside of his younger colleague whom he dearly loved.

"I am sorry to die," sighed Pasteur, "I wanted to do so much for my country."

A week later a cousin wrote: "The news is rather good this morning; the patient was able to sleep for a few hours last night, which he had not yet done.... All scientific Paris comes anxiously to inquire after the patient; intimate friends take turns in watching by him. Dumas, the great chemist, was affectionately insisting on taking his turn yesterday. Every morning the Emperor and Empress send a footman for news, which Dr. Godelier gives him in a sealed envelope. . . ."

That same day, just a week after the stroke which nearly killed him, Pasteur insisted upon dictating a note to one of his collaborators sitting at his bedside. The communication outlined an ingenious method for the early detection of flacherie. The next day, at the meeting of members of the Academy, Dumas read Pasteur's memorandum, which for a moment seemed to bring him back into their midst.

Before his illness construction of the new laboratory had begun, and now as he lay in bed, his body prostrate but his mind ever active, he listened in vain to catch noises of workmen which might be heard just across the courtyard.

"How are they getting on?" he asked. Mme. Pasteur went to the window and returned with a vague answer, for the day after his stroke, workmen had disappeared. Pasteur finally became suspicious and one night gave vent to bitter feelings:

"How much more straightforward it would have been to have announced that they expected me to die, and that work on the building would be suspended!"

His distress was reported to Napoleon, who ordered the work resumed at once.

A few weeks later, Pasteur walked from his bed to an armchair for the first time. His left leg was rigid, his left arm bent and the fingers tightly clenched. The thought of such a tragedy in his forty-sixth year sometimes overcame him, but he struggled to conquer the melancholy fears that he might never work again. As the weeks passed, he walked with less and less assistance, although his leg remained stiff and his hand useless. The task of walking with a cane became easier.

Three months after the stroke, he declared himself fit and ready to work. Physicians and friends begged him to take a few months more to rest, but he would not listen to their warnings. He must complete his work with silkworms at once, for to delay any longer would postpone his final conclusions another whole year. With his wife and daughter, Marie-Louise, he started on January 18 for St. Hippolyte le Fort, near Alès where tests were to be made on worms forced to mature early.

This time he was not the first to be up in the morning to pick fresh mulberry leaves or start a new experiment. His assistants came to his bedside in the morning and received instructions for the day's work, and in the evening they returned to report results. During the morning his wife generally read the newspaper to him. If he felt especially well, he would walk in the garden in the afternoon. He often dictated notes to her for a book he was writing on silkworm culture. Mme. Pasteur and his little eleven-year-old daughter saw to it that he did not overdo, and he wrote that Marie-Louise "pitilessly takes books, pens, papers and pencils away from me with a perseverance which causes me joy and despair."

Data began to pile up, and the conclusions became clear. The breeding was successful and all his predictions had come true. He could now rejoice that he had not given in to the warnings of his physicians, and that in spite of all his physical handicaps his scientific work could still go on.

When April came, he went with his family to Alès to collect further data on the results of that year's breeding. His two assistants left for distant magnaneries to observe the hatching of broods cultivated by Pasteurian methods. Similar observations began at Alès. His collaborators returned, and Dumas arrived to learn that in 200 broods, from three different sources and hatched in various localities, there was not a single failure.

The epidemic was conquered, and Pasteur believed that now all he need do was report his final conclusions. But he was wrong. False rumors were still being spread by those who had purchased eggs from Japan at a high price and saw their business ruined. Pasteur had toiled for five years to save the industry and help the peasants recover their earnings. He had worked in spite of great personal sorrow, and tremendous physical handicaps. All this he could do, but he was overcome with sadness and indignation to know that falsehoods and jealousies still persisted. He longed to see his methods used everywhere.

Marshall Valliant had followed Pasteur's work with intelligent interest. Eager to give official support, he suggested to Napoleon that Pasteur spend several months at an old villa in Italy close to Trieste near the border of the Adriatic. Villa Vicentina, owned by Napoleon, had once been a prosperous center for silkworm culture, but for ten years the fifty tenants living on the Emperor's estate had hardly been able to raise a single healthy cocoon because of pébrine and flacherie. The mulberry trees, once known as "Trees of Gold," came to leaf in the spring and were bare in the winter, but the peasants' pockets remained empty of gold.   Napoleon invited Pasteur to spend several months at Villa Vicentina.

The plan was hailed by everyone as an excellent suggestion.   Life in the quiet countryside would help restore Pasteur's health, and he would restore the silkworm industry to this devastated region.   Success here would give imperial sanction to his methods and put an end to false rumors.   Pasteur and his wife arrived in November of 1869, bringing selected eggs from Alès.   Raulin, his assistant, joined them later.

Pasteur spent seven months, not resting, but working in an atmosphere of great calm as he went about reorganizing the magnanerie and starting the breeding.   Under a blue sky in this mild climate, Pasteur completed the dictation of his two-volume book covering all his studies on silkworm culture.   Before he left, he presented the Emperor with a rich harvest of beautiful cocoons which would bring a net profit of 22,000 francs—the first profit from this region for ten years.   The economy of the tenants was now restored, and they hailed Pasteur as their benefactor.

On his return to Paris, he stopped at Munich to pay a visit to Liebig, his former adversary on the role of microbes in fermentation.   Surely, after thirteen years, this venerable German chemist must have come to accept the Pasteurian doctrine.   As Pasteur limped into his laboratory, Liebig rose and received him with kindly courtesy, but when Pasteur tried to discuss the chemical reactions of fermentation, Liebig remained silent.   Pasteur did not press him.

He made another stop at Strasbourg, so full of happy

memories of his five years as professor at the university. The city was in turmoil with rumors of impending war with Germany. He could not believe what he heard, for no hint of war had reached him. He left the city, deeply saddened and shocked that his hopes for peace, which he naively believed could be founded on progress through science, were now about to be completely shattered.

A few days after his arrival in Paris, the French government officially declared war against Germany, on July 19, 1870. Although some people believed that Napoleon had committed many political errors at home and abroad, Pasteur looked upon the Emperor's reign "as the most glorious" in the history of France. To him the invasion of France by Prussia was nothing short of an atrocity. Others, who could criticize the aging Emperor, believed that he committed his greatest blunder in leading France, so completely unprepared, into war against her ancient enemy. News of one defeat after another came pouring into Paris.

On September 1, Napoleon was taken prisoner, and the Second Empire collapsed. France was declared a republic, and the new government found it impossible to end the war. Troops departed from Paris and the unprotected city prepared for siege. Every student at the Ecole Normale enlisted even though he might have claimed exemption from military service. The buildings of the Ecole were converted into a hospital and residence for those Normaliens who were stationed in Paris.

Pasteur was eager to join the *garde nationale,* but what possible service could he be with only one good arm and one good leg? Everyone begged him to leave the city. He appealed to Dr. Godelier:

"I cannot fight, but I can stay and serve France with my work in the laboratory."

"You have no right to stay," answered the doctor. Then with a twinkle in his eye, he added: "You would only be a useless mouth to feed."

On September 4, Pasteur, accompanied by his wife and Marie-Louise, took refuge in Arbois. Jean-Baptiste, who was eighteen years old, had already left Paris to join the ranks of the Eastern Army Corps.

In the old tannery at Arbois, Pasteur found laboratory work practically impossible. As he watched his sister Virginie knead and bake the bread, he studied the role of yeast and the influence of air on the rising dough. He tried to discover new ways of increasing the nutritive value of bread and lower its price. Observing Virginie's husband at work in the tannery, he studied the fermentation of the tanning fluid.

Day after day at the sound of a trumpet, the people of Arbois rushed to the streets to hear news reported by the village crier. It was never good: retreat, defeat, surrender. Pasteur stood with the crowds by the bridge over the Cuisance River and remembered stories of the days when Jean-Joseph had fought for Napoleon I only to see his country vanquished. He missed his father now, but was glad he had not lived to see France again humiliated. Before the end of September, the city of Strasbourg, which the French had considered a stronghold of resistance, was forced to capitulate.

Surrounded by German troops, Paris was besieged. Pasteur, so kindly, so humane, so admiring of German scientists became embittered. He wrote to one of his assistants: "Every one of my future works will bear on its title page the words 'Hatred to Prussia! Revenge! Revenge!'"

On January 9, during the siege of Paris, the Prussians bombarded the Museum of Natural History, which "until then had been respected by all parties and all powers, national or foreign." When news of this outrage reached Pasteur, he knew he must find some way to give vent to his indignation. What could he do? Suddenly he remembered the honorary degree of Doctor of Medicine bestowed upon him by the German university at Bonn. He would return it. To the head of the faculty of medicine, he wrote: "While affirming my profound respect for you, Sir, and for the celebrated professors who have affixed their signatures to the decision of the members of your Order, I am called upon by my conscience to ask you to efface my name from the archives of your Faculté, and to take back that diploma, as a sign of the indignation inspired in a French scientist by the barbarity and hypocrisy of him [King Wilhelm of Prussia] who, in order to satisfy his criminal pride, persists in the massacre of two great nations."

Jean-Baptiste's battalion was engaged in fighting near the Swiss border. The fighting had been desperate, and the regiment was ordered to turn back toward Dôle. The officer in command, unable to bear the sight of the suffering soldiers, chose the town of Pontarlier as a last line of retreat. Confusion spread as many lost their way through the snow-filled roads, and the exhausted soldiers, hungry and shivering, were begging food from door to door. No word came from Jean-Baptiste.

One day, Pasteur announced that he had hired a carriage and that the next morning he would start in search of his son. In the morning, Mme. Pasteur had her announcement to make:

"Marie-Louise and I will go with you. You cannot travel alone."

Pasteur's old friend, Jules Vercel, bid the anxious family farewell as they set out for Pontarlier in an old dilapidated carriage on that cold Tuesday morning, January 24, 1871. Progress was slow through the snowy roads, and that night they slept in an inn near Montrond. Wednesday they stayed in Censeau and Thursday at Chaffois. On Friday they reached Pontarlier to find the town full of retreating soldiers. Many of the sick and wounded were trying to warm themselves over fires built by the roadside. The anxious family scanned every face. No one had news of Jean-Baptiste.

"All I can tell you," said one, "is that out of his battalion of 1,200 men there are only 300 left."

Another, hearing the name Pasteur, called out: "Sargeant Pasteur? Yes, he is alive. I slept by him last night at Chaffois. He is only slightly ill and remained behind. You might meet him on the road toward Chaffois."

The searching party started back toward Chaffois, and just as they passed through the gates of Pontarlier, they met an open wagon coming toward them. It was full of soldiers. There, standing against the side of the wagon, was Jean-Baptiste, who gasped when he saw his family. Strong enough to jump to the road, he rushed to his father who came limping toward him. Father and son embraced in true French fashion, but for a moment neither could speak. They took the exhausted boy to Geneva and after several days of rest and adequate food, he was able to return to his unit.

For four months Paris had resisted siege. Finally in January, hunger forced its citizens to open negotiations for surrender. The conditions of peace were finally ratified in Bordeaux on March 1, and Alsace-Lorraine was annexed to Germany. Thus the ancient city of Strasbourg fell to the German Empire, and Pasteur never returned to the place where he was married and started his career as a university professor.

Pasteur wrote to his assistant on March 29: "My head is brimming with splendid projects. The war sent my brain to pasture. I am now ready for new projects. . . . How fortunate you are to be young and strong! Why can I not begin a new life of study and work? Unhappy France, beloved country, if I could only assist in raising thee from thy disasters!"

Indeed he could and did, for his greatest contributions to the welfare of mankind were still to be made.

CHAPTER 12

In Search of the Culprit

AFTER the Franco-Prussian War, Pasteur had hoped to return to Paris and begin work on contagious diseases, but he was advised to wait. One wing of the Ecole Normale had been destroyed, and its reconstruction was still incomplete. Dormitories and classrooms were occupied by hundreds of the wounded and sick, and his laboratories were filled with refugees. He contented himself by going to Clermont-Ferrand for a short time to work on the more prosaic study of the souring of beer. He was able to give men in the breweries the same answer he had made to the wine merchants: beer could be preserved by "pasteurization" without damage to its flavor. Although he soon returned to Paris, his work on contagious diseases was further delayed for three or four years.

Poor health made it impossible for Pasteur to hold his two positions—director of the laboratory at the Ecole Normale, and professor of organic chemistry at the Sorbonne. He resigned from the latter, for he could not think of giving up his research. In 1874 the National Assembly of the French government, by a vote of 532 to 24, granted him an annual pension of 12,000 francs for the rest of his life. This approximated the salary he forfeited at the Sorbonne and enabled him to devote his entire time to research. One member of the Assembly wrote that Pasteur's discoveries had not only brought glory to France but had assured the nation of millions of francs "without retaining the least share of them for himself."

Congratulations came pouring in: "Where is the government," wrote his old friend Chappuis, who was now president of the Grenoble Academy, "which has secured such a majority?" From Sainte Claire Deville: "Bravo, my dear Pasteur: I am glad for you and for myself, and proud for all of us." From one of his collaborators: "You are going to be a happy scientist, for you can already see, and you will see more and more, the triumphs of your doctrines and your discoveries."

Some of his friends believed this last honor represented the final chapter of his glorious life. Nicard, the former director of the Ecole Normale, wrote: "Now, dear friend, you must give up your energies to living for your family, for all those who love you, and a little too for yourself." His physician forbade him any strenuous labor. All these warnings only served to greatly irritate Pasteur, for he considered that life without work missed the purpose of living.

At the time Pasteur established the role of microbes in fermentation, he quickly saw a comparison between the "germ theory of fermentation" and the germ theory of contagious diseases. As early as 1859, while writing about fermentation brought about by living microbes, he had said, "Everything indicates that contagious diseases owe their existence to similar causes." Again in the following year he predicted that his work on spontaneous generation and the origin of microbes "would prepare the road for a serious investigation of the origin of various diseases." When he wrote to Napoleon III in 1865, requesting better laboratory facilities, he had said that his work on wines opened new vistas in medicine. In order to study the causes of contagious diseases he had asked for adequate buildings for "the housing of animals, either dead or alive."

Thus by 1870, no one was better prepared than Pasteur to undertake the study of diseases caused by microbes. But it was Lord Lister, an English surgeon working in a Glasgow hospital, who first demonstrated the medical significance of Pasteur's work.

Surgical wards of those days were filled with putrid odors of decaying wounds. The number of deaths resulting from gangrene and blood poisoning was appallingly high. Indeed, the most skillful physicians dreaded to operate. Lister felt helpless in combating an unknown and unseen enemy that paraded his surgical ward.

He read Pasteur's studies on fermentation and decay. "If microbes can cause decay," Lister reasoned, "they might be the cause of gangrene in decaying wounds; and if dust particles in the air are laden with microbes, these might drop into an operating wound."

Inspired by these ideas, Lister began at once to develop his antiseptic surgical technique, and invented a carbolic acid spray which was directed into the air surrounding the field of operation. When he started to operate, he took off his coat, rolled up his sleeves, pinned a towel over his waistcoat, and dipped his hands into carbolic acid. When the patient fell asleep from breathing chloroform, he washed the skin of the operating area with carbolic acid, turned on the spray and began to operate. These elaborate techniques were ridiculed by other surgeons who regarded his methods as merely a new notion in wound treatment, whereas Lister was actually establishing principles that form the basis of modern aseptic surgery. Sometime after he began to use these antiseptic methods, he reported that in a nine-month period not a case of gangrene had developed in his ward.

In 1874, nine years after he started his new method, Lister wrote to Pasteur: "Allow me to take this opportunity to tender you my most cordial thanks for having by your brilliant researches demonstrated the truth of the germ theory of putrifaction and thus furnished me with the principle upon which alone the antiseptic system can be carried out. Should you at any time visit Edinburgh, it would, I believe, give you sincere gratification to see at our hospital how largely mankind is being benefited by your labours. . . ."

At the outbreak of the Franco-Prussian War, Lister had been using his antiseptic methods for five years. A French medical student who had journeyed to Scotland in 1869 published in a French surgical journal a description of Lister's method of "extreme and minute care in dressing wounds." But French surgeons were too well satisfied with their own methods to pay any heed to the news of

Lister's success, and thousands of wounded French soldiers who might have been saved, died of gangrene.

The culprits of "hospital pus" and gangrene had been conquered, but there were other unseen enemies that stalked the land. Various fevers—malaria, typhoid, typhus, yellow fever—spread from man to man in army tents. Epidemics of cholera often moved from city to city. A ship left port with healthy men aboard only to return with half its crew. The others had died at sea.

If these diseases and deaths were due to microbes that could invade the human body, the dangerous germs must be spotted among the many harmless ones that were known to live in the nose and throat and digestive system. If the lives of men, women and children were ever to be saved from these enemies, these culprits must first be found. But many physicians continued to argue that these plagues arose from some vague cause within the body. It was fantastic, they insisted, to think they were caused by the invasion of germs from the outside.

The search for the causative agent in contagious diseases was and is beset with many difficult problems. The mere presence of a particular microbe in the sick person does not alone constitute proof. Somehow the suspected microbe must be removed from the sick person and produce disease when injected into a healthy, susceptible test animal. For Pasteur, the study of contagious diseases was especially difficult, for he was neither a veterinarian nor a physician, and members of these professions would not make it easy for him to enter their fields. In 1873, he was elected by a majority of one vote to the French Academy of Medicine. This would give him some prestige in the medical world and help him to undertake medical studies. He promised himself that he would regularly attend all meetings of the Academy. When he went to his first meeting and quietly limped to the seat assigned to him, no one realized that the greatest revolutionary in the history of medicine had joined their ranks. He was ready to study contagious diseases, but where should he begin?

The agriculture of France and many European nations was threatened by large numbers of sheep dying of *anthrax*. This disease mysteriously spread among the animals, sometimes killing half a flock. A stricken animal would suddenly lag behind the others, shaking and gasping for breath, only to die within a few hours. Sometimes, a sheep would collapse before the shepherd had had time even to notice the attack. Certain fields were considered cursed by evil spirits, for sheep grazing there seemed doomed to die of anthrax. Some farms were called "anthrax farms."

During the middle of the nineteenth century, despite popular hostility to the germ theory of disease, a few physicians and veterinarians attempted to prove that microbes alone could initiate disease in a healthy body. In 1845, a French physician, Davaine, saw motionless, microscopic rods (bacilli) in the blood of animals dead from anthrax, but did not attach any significance to them. Ten years later, Pollender saw the same tiny rods, and asked himself if these microbes might not be the causative agent of anthrax. Other workers said "no," because sometimes their test animals had either died without showing any rods or showed ones that differed from those of Davaine.

In 1861, after reading Pasteur's paper on fermentation,

Davaine changed his opinion and concluded that the motile bacilli he had described seven years earlier must, after all, be the cause of this deadly disease. His conclusion was based on the fact that the rods were continuously present during the disease, that inoculation of anthrax blood produced the disease in test animals, and that the disease did not appear unless the rods were present. But many workers still criticized the validity of Davaine's conclusions because, like others, some of their animals had died without showing the typical rods of Davaine. And there the matter stood.

In 1877, in the midst of all this confusion, Dr. Robert Koch published an account of his work on anthrax which soon became a classic. From now on, answers to the cause of this deadly disease could not be reported as *opinions* based on speculation or faulty experiments. The search for the microbic enemy must be conducted with the greatest technical precision.

Dr. Koch was a German physician who had enlisted as a surgeon in the Franco-Prussian War. After completing his services, he went to Woolstein, a small village in Prussia, where he established a busy medical practice. Here, working alone in a small laboratory, a screened-off portion of the room where he received his patients, he began his study of anthrax.

The flaw in the work of Davaine, Pollender, and others had been their failure to isolate the anthrax germ and work with it and it alone. They had inoculated drops of anthrax blood into test animals, but had no proof that their results were necessarily due to the rods because there was no telling what other factor in the blood might also have been injected.

It was on this point that Koch's work surpassed that of all previous workers. He was able to grow the rods outside the animal body in a drop of sterile fluid removed from the eye of an experimental animal. Hour by hour he watched these motionless rods (now called *Bacillus anthracis*) under the microscope. Within twenty hours, they became long and slender—almost twenty times their original length so that they looked like a ball of entangled threads. Gradually these threads became punctuated with tiny dots, especially in those rods found at the edge of the drop where the oxygen was most abundant.

Koch recognized that these dots, which looked like peas in a pod, were bacterial spores—seedlike forms which develop in certain bacteria under unfavorable conditions. When living conditions improve, spores are able to germinate into growing microbes. Thus, Koch described for the first time the life history of *Bacillus anthracis* from spores to the motionless rods which divided by simply splitting. The microbe grew best in the absence of free oxygen and was therefore one of the anaerobic organisms described by Pasteur some years previously.

Koch was now able to explain "anthrax farms." The bodies of sheep that had died of anthrax were left in the fields to disintegrate and contaminated the ground with anthrax rods. Under the unfavorable conditions of life in the soil, the bacilli formed spores that survived until they could enter the bodies of healthy sheep that grazed there. That is, the spores entered the sheep with the grass they

ate, and then germinated into rods that multiplied and
spread throughout the blood stream.

Koch then turned to experimental studies. He injected
test animals—guinea pigs and mice—with cultures of the
anthrax rods, which caused their death as rapidly as
though they had been inoculated with anthrax blood.

Anthrax bacilli
with nonstaining spores

He took one further step in tracking down the culprit.
Into one drop of his nutrient fluid, he placed a drop of
anthrax blood. After the rods had increased in number,
he took a sample of this drop and placed it into a second
drop of sterile fluid. This was called the first transplant.
Repeating this eight times, he found that injections of the
eighth transplant resulted in the death of the animal as
readily as an injection of the first culture containing a drop
of anthrax blood.

Despite the refinement of Koch's techniques, it did
leave a loophole for the skeptics to attack. "What evidence was there," they asked, "that some theoretical factor

other than the rods had not been carried from the blood into the eighth transplant?" This jury of unbelievers insisted upon more absolute proof before accusing *Bacillus anthracis*. At this point, Pasteur entered the controversy.

Working with his assistant, Joubert, in the new laboratory at the Ecole Normale, Pasteur hunted for a different nutrient fluid in which to grow the deadly rods. A culture medium, which could be obtained in larger quantities than the drops of fluid used by Koch, was needed. Pursuing one idea after another, Pasteur found that sterile, nonacid urine met this requirement.

He then placed a drop of anthrax blood in a flask containing 50 cubic centimeters (two ounces) of sterile urine and obtained a culture seething with the living rods. One drop of this culture transplanted into another flask of 50 cubic centimeters of urine constituted the first transplant. After waiting for the bacteria to multiply, Pasteur took a drop of the first transplant and inoculated another flask containing 50 cubic centimeters of urine. This constituted the second transplant. He repeated this procedure one hundred times so that the original drop of blood in the first culture had been diluted as much as one part in 100^{100}. A dilution as great as this reaches a figure of such magnitude that the mind cannot possibly conceive it, containing, as it does, 300 zeros. If such a figure were to be printed out on this page, it would stretch across its width about five times. The dilution was greater than a drop of blood lost in the oceans of the world.

An injection of this one hundredth-transplant rapidly killed the animal, and the dilution was of such enormous magnitude that it ruled out any possibility of injecting even a single molecule of the original blood. The only agents which could not escape dilution were the living microbes which multiplied in each transplant.

Pasteur performed another ingenious experiment to test the possible presence of some living agent (other than the rods) which might be too small to be seen through the microscope. If any such agent had been present in his dilution experiment, they too would have multiplied and escaped dilution. As he struggled with this problem, it occurred to him to filter a culture of anthrax rods through a membrane which would hold back all visible microbes. Only living agents which might be too small for the microscope to reveal could pass through. When this clear fluid, that was free from any visible microbes, was injected into a rabbit, the animal remained in perfect health.

Anthrax was not caused by some microscopically invisible living agent. It was not caused by some vague factor in the blood. It was caused by the microscopically *visible Bacillus anthracis,* and by it alone.

The joint efforts of Koch and Pasteur had done more than prove that the rods of Davaine are the causative agent in anthrax. They had established the germ theory of disease and started it on its way to becoming a doctrine.

The science of bacteriology had now reached a point where the need for a simple method for obtaining a pure culture of any organism (a culture of only one type of microbe) was of prime importance. So far, only liquid media had been used for growing bacteria, and the process of getting pure cultures in such a medium was a laborious and time-consuming task. Koch, always a master hand in technical matters, invented a type of food for cultivating bacteria known as *solid media*. By adding gelatin to a nutrient fluid, the medium hardened and a single bacterium growing on it formed colonies that could clearly be seen without the use of a microscope. Koch inserted a sterile needle into a colony and transplanted the material into liquid broth. By this simple method, he was able to obtain a pure culture of microbes that had all descended from the original bacterium from which the colony had developed. A fundamental step for future work in precise bacteriological techniques had now been taken.

When Koch demonstrated this simple method of "fishing" from a single colony to Pasteur in 1881 at the International Congress of Medicine which met in London, Pasteur exclaimed. "This is tremendous progress!" Ten years earlier he had expressed hatred for Prussia, but in the face of a great contribution to science made by one German investigator, he felt nothing but admiration.

The disease of anthrax was the touchstone which established beyond any shadow of a doubt that a microscopic living organism can invade a healthy body millions of times larger than itself and by its growth initiate a fatal disease. The work of Koch and Pasteur made it clear that future scientists searching for the causative agent of other diseases must pursue the quest with great technical precision. Koch formulated laws which must be followed in such searches. His postulates prevented these studies, which were so popular in the late nineteenth century, from becoming chaotic and unscientific. Koch's postulates state:

1. The microbe must be found in every case of the specific disease.

2. The microbe must be recovered in pure culture.

3. The introduction of the organism from pure culture into a healthy, susceptible animal must reproduce the disease.

4. From the experimentally infected animal, the same microbe must again be recovered.

For Pasteur, his work on contagious diseases had only begun. The anthrax culprit had been found, but the important task lay ahead. How could this microbic enemy be prevented from doing its deadly work?

CHAPTER 13

The Happy Accident

REQUESTS to study various diseases came pouring into Pasteur's laboratory. He had always worked on several problems at a time, but now he was busier than ever. Physicians were calling him out of the laboratory and into the hospitals. The suffering of sick and dying patients was very painful for him to watch, and sometimes he could not stay in a sickroom. But if he were to widen the horizon of his research, he must go to the bedside of the sick and take samples of blood, pus, or gangrenous tissue, and return to his laboratory with these specimens. He must examine these samples under the microscope, isolate the germs and culture them. There was no end to the number of studies he might do, but one question still dominated all his thinking: how could sheep be saved from anthrax?

Pasteur often went about his laboratory as though in a dream. At least this was the impression he made when deeply concentrating upon some problem. He seemed lost to the world during periods of meditation when he made notes of new ideas, new questions, new experiments, and new theories that must be tested. He always insisted upon absolute quiet in the laboratory, and there were moments when his assistants knew that they must not interrupt him even with important questions. These times came often now, for he was pondering morning, noon, and night on the problem of protecting sheep from anthrax.

The success of Jenner's smallpox vaccine was constantly on his mind. He read about it, reasoned with it, and tried to understand it. One hundred years earlier this British physician had vaccinated many people in England with fluid taken from cowpox sores on milkmaids' hands. When a smallpox epidemic spread through a village, the vaccinated people escaped the deadly disease. Jenner's vaccine worked, but no one could explain how. Pasteur tried to. Were the smallpox microbe and the cowpox microbe one and the same organism, or were they different? What happened to the smallpox germ when it multiplied in the cow? Did growth in the cow weaken it? How could anthrax rods be made weaker? Could resistant anthrax spores ever be controlled?

Pasteur's work with silkworms had sharpened his ideas about diseases caused by microbes. He saw the process as an interrelation between two living things: the host (the silkworm) and the invading microbes (the corpuscles of pébrine). The disease itself expressed this conflict between host and invader, a conflict in which each was trying to survive. The outcome depended upon many factors. The primary cause was the invading microbe, but this germ must be able to grow and multiply in the host to produce the disease.

A host might be strong and resist the growth of the invading organism, or so weak that the invader could rapidly increase in number and conquer its host. The resistance of the silkworm, for instance, was weakened by exposure to sudden changes in temperature. The strength of the enemy was increased when worms were fed rotting mulberry leaves, because then millions of flacherie germs entered the host with the food.

Could anthrax rods ever be controlled? If he could protect sheep from anthrax, Pasteur felt he might then discover how to protect mankind from various contagious diseases.

As he tried to plan a campaign against anthrax, he was interrupted at every turn. One of his assistants was suffering from a boil on the neck. Using strict aseptic techniques, Pasteur removed the pus and studied it under the microscope. There he saw not rods, but tiny spheres (cocci) arranged in clusters. He called them "bunches of grapes" (*staphylococci*). He cultured these germs and injected them under the skin of a guinea pig, and promptly the animal developed abscesses at the points of injection. These staphylococci were the causative agent of the abscess of his assistant.

Staphylococci

Another interruption followed when he was called to the Trousseau hospital in Paris to examine pus in the bone of a young girl. As the surgeon operated, exposing the bone, Pasteur took a sample of pus. Returning with it to the laboratory, he studied it under the microscope. Again he saw "bunches of grapes." These staphylococci could not only cause pus in the skin but could also invade the body, enter the bones and form pus in deeper regions.

In Paris, one of the maternity hospitals was forced to close because deaths of mothers following childbirth ran so high. The disease resembled blood poisoning. Pasteur took samples of blood from these unfortunate mothers back to the laboratory. Again his microscope showed tiny spheres, not arranged in clusters but in chains, like beads in a necklace. These were called *streptococci,* and they caused the blood poisoning of childbirth fever.

More than thirty years earlier, long before the advent of the germ theory of disease, Dr. Oliver Wendell Holmes in Boston and Dr. Semmelweis in Budapest had tried to teach young doctors that childbirth fever was spread from patient to patient by the unclean hands of nurses and physicians. But the words of Holmes and Semmelweis

Streptococci

went unheeded. Now, Pasteur *saw* the microbe about which these older physicians had so shrewdly speculated.

Shortly after Pasteur had studied these streptococci, a doctor lectured before the Academy of Medicine on childbirth fever. He spoke in vague terms about its causes, emphasizing overcrowding and foul air in hospital wards. Pasteur, unable to contain himself, vigorously interrupted:

"You are wrong, my colleague. Nothing that you have mentioned are causes of childbirth fever. It is due to a microbe introduced into the mother at the time of delivery by the contaminated hands of doctors and nurses."

"But this imaginary microbe you speak of will never be found," responded the speaker.

Pasteur sprang from his seat. Forgetting his cane, he rushed to the blackboard dragging his stiff leg, grabbed a piece of chalk and drew several spheres in chainlike formation.

"There—that's what it looks like," thundered Pasteur, who was by nature so quiet and gentle. However, when forced to defend the truth as he saw it, he never failed to confront his adversaries with aggressive confidence.

A short time later, at the Academy of Sciences, he described his work on a disease in hens which often killed 90 per cent of a flock. He said: "There sometimes appears in poultry yards a destructive disease by the name of chicken cholera. The bird affected by it is feeble, and staggers about with drooping wings. Its ruffled feathers give it the shape of a ball. It is seized with overpowering drowsiness, and if one forces it to open its eyes it appears to wake from a deep sleep; the lids soon close again, and usually death occurs after a short mute agony, without the creature having changed its position."

Several workers had seen a microbe in the blood of hens dead from chicken cholera, but they had been unable to make cultures of it, and no one had proof that it was the causative agent of the disease. Professor Toussaint of the Veterinary School of Toulouse sent Pasteur the head of a cock that had died from chicken cholera. At once Pasteur studied it and found a type of microbe which appeared as "tiny bodies, extremely slender and constricted in the middle." Here was another disease-producing rod—another kind of a bacillus, which differed from anthrax rods in many ways. For one thing, it did not form spores.

Toussaint had tried in vain to grow the germ in nonacid urine. Pasteur found that chicken broth provided an excellent medium for the growth of these chicken cholera rods. Healthy hens inoculated with a pure culture of this microbe perished in twenty-four to forty-eight hours. Even a tiny drop of the culture spread over a few crumbs and fed to hens resulted in immediate death. The microbe therefore entered the host through the digestive system and spread to the blood stream. The excreta of an infected hen contained the deadly germ, and healthy hens living in the same cage with an infected one contracted the disease by feeding on food contaminated with such excreta.

Pasteur made several other unusual observations. Guinea pigs inoculated with cultures of the chicken cholera bacilli developed an abscess at the point of injection, and recovered without developing any other sign of illness. But rabbits and hens living in contact with these guinea pigs succumbed to the disease when the abscesses ruptured and contaminated the food. As Pasteur explained: "An observer witnessing these facts and ignorant of the above-mentioned cause, would be astonished to see hens die without apparent cause, and would believe in the spontaneity of the evil, for he would be far from supposing that it had its origin in the guinea pigs, all of them in good health."

Pasteur had never been busier than he was during these years when his laboratory was flooded with experiments on anthrax, abscesses in bone and skin, childbirth fever, and chicken cholera. The only moments of relaxation came on Sunday evenings when the Pasteur apartment at the Ecole Normale was filled with young people who had been invited to dinner. Special invitations were sent each week to students at the Ecole and to friends of Marie-Louise and Jean-Baptiste.

Pasteur looked forward to these meetings when he could talk with young people about postwar conditions in France. One week, Mme. Pasteur had just finished reading to him the first book by a young man named René Vallery-Radot. The writing revealed a patriotism which stirred Pasteur, who then and there decided he must meet the young author.

To René's complete surprise, he received an invitation to attend one of the Pasteur Sunday dinners. As a student of literature, René knew little about science, and to prepare himself for this important meeting, he read everything he could find about Pasteur's work on spontaneous generation, little knowing that Pasteur wanted to talk with him about his beloved country and about people of the literary world.   Fearfully he went to meet the great scientist and his family.

At first he was intimidated by Pasteur's gravity and his sad expression.   His clear, penetrating gaze seemed to look right through him, but the moment Pasteur spoke, René felt his warmth and kindliness.   The benevolence of Mme. Pasteur and the gaiety of Jean-Baptiste soon made him feel at ease.

From that day forth René Vallery-Radot was a frequent visitor at the Pasteur home.   Everyone had come to respect and love him, and he and Marie-Louise had fallen in love. Three years later, in 1879, René became the beloved husband of Marie-Louise and the devoted son-in-law of her parents, who rejoiced that René had joined the happy family circle.

During Pasteur's declining years, his son-in-law was his constant companion.   He journeyed with him to many international scientific conferences, escorted him to meetings in Paris, and during the summer holidays walked with him over the country roads at Arbois.   Upstairs in the old tannery, the two men worked side by side at their desks, Pasteur revising a scientific paper while René completed some literary work.   Marie-Louise and her mother had always watched over Pasteur, and now René joined in helping him devote his entire life to science.

Pasteur spent the summer months of 1879 in Arbois. Cultures of chicken cholera were left in the laboratory at the Ecole Normale, and Pasteur charged his two assistants to keep the microbes alive by making frequent transplants into sterile chicken broth. But the two assistants took a short holiday, and the cultures were neglected.

When they returned, they injected a hen with an aging culture, and to their complete amazement the animal lived. Quickly they obtained a fresh, vigorous culture and injected it into the same hen. Again, to their even greater bewilderment, the hen lived. What could possibly have happened? What had gone wrong? What would Pasteur say when he returned and learned about this? Anxiously they waited for Pasteur.

When he heard this news, Pasteur was for a moment silent. Then he burst forth: "Ah, this is wonderful. The secret has been found! The old culture protected the hen against the virulent germ. Hens can be vaccinated against chicken cholera."

By the happiest accident, his assistants had allowed the chicken cholera rods to age slowly and die. But it was no accident that Pasteur could at once explain everything. For twenty years, ever since he had demonstrated the "germ theory of fermentation," he had believed in the germ theory of disease. Having found the anthrax rods, he thought of little else than how he might protect sheep from this disease. Pasteur had often said that "Chance favors only the mind that is prepared." The chance neglect of his assistants provided the prepared mind of Pasteur with the solution to the vaccination problem. Often his active imagination had shot through a mass of confused facts and revealed the solution to some pressing problem. Again his genius served him.

What Pasteur had seen in a flash now took months of the

most careful work to prove. What specific factor had caused the microbes to age and die? It soon became clear that the older the culture, the weaker the bacilli became. Time was a factor, but what was the responsible agent? With his characteristic ability to note the slightest detail, Pasteur observed that culture tubes which had been sealed and thus kept free from air, did not weaken—did not age —whereas tubes plugged with cotton and thus exposed to the air grew weaker as each day passed. Furthermore, a culture of known, measured weakness when transplanted into fresh broth maintained the same degree of weakness. In other words, the loss of toxic property was a hereditary change passed on to future generations of the bacilli.

He now could weaken chicken cholera rods at will and obtain a measurable degree of loss of toxicity. By vaccinating hens with cultures of known weakness, he protected hens from the disease. All technical aspects had now been solved, and he worked out a vaccination program which he could control with precision and certainty.

At last Pasteur was ready to turn his energies to the problem of vaccinating sheep against anthrax. This would obviously be a much more difficult problem, for unlike the chicken-cholera bacilli, anthrax rods developed spores when exposed to oxygen. How could these deadly rods be cultivated and yet their ability to form spores destroyed? He must somehow prevent spores from developing in a growing culture. This called for an entirely new method of procedure.

With all his inventive capacities at work, Pasteur tried one method after another. He turned to growing anthrax rods at different temperatures. Disease germs grow best at 37 degrees centigrade, which is slightly above the normal temperature of the human body (98 degrees Fahrenheit). When he grew anthrax cultures at temperatures as high as 42 to 43 degrees centigrade (107 to 109 degrees Fahrenheit), the rods multiplied but never formed spores. Furthermore, a culture maintained at this temperature for one week developed slender rods which had become so weakened that injections of them into sheep were harmless. Again he had solved the problem. He could protect sheep from anthrax! He could hardly contain himself with joy.

Making further tests, he found that it was advisable to give sheep two vaccines, the first one from a culture with very low toxicity followed, twelve days later, by a slightly more toxic one. Future benefits to mankind now spread before his imagination in full glory, and he gave vent to his feelings in the poetic words: "The breath of Truth is carrying it [his doctrine of vaccination] toward the fruitful fields of the future."

Once more, however, Pasteur had to face rigid opposition. Veterinary surgeons felt their profession had been invaded by an outsider, and farmers had too often been deceived by some false promise of remedy to be fooled again. Skeptics violently voiced their doubts.

The Agricultural Society of Melun (a small town a few miles south of Paris) suggested that a public demonstration of anthrax vaccination be made at Pouilly-le-Fort, a farm near Melun owned by M. Rossignol, a veterinary surgeon. Pasteur welcomed the chance to prove to the world the truth of his work, and on April 22, 1881, he drafted and signed a plan in which every detail of the procedure was described. His two assistants, Chamberland and Roux, were called back from their vacation. In the laboratory they met Pasteur who described to them the full details of this public demonstration.

They would use fifty sheep. These would be divided into two lots of twenty-five each. Lot 1 would receive two anthrax vaccinations, the second to be given ten or twelve days after the first. About two weeks later, all fifty sheep would receive injections of living anthrax rods from the most toxic culture.

"A few days later, all vaccinated sheep will be in perfect health; all unvaccinated ones will be dead," said Pasteur.

"But this is a most exacting test," responded his assistants. "It is so stiff that it allows for not a single exception. But you have signed the agreement, M. Pasteur, and there's nothing to do but go ahead."

"What succeeded with fourteen sheep in the laboratory will be equally successful with fifty at Melun," answered Pasteur with complete confidence.

On May 5, 1881, Chamberland and Roux started for Melun to begin the vaccination experiment.

"Whatever you do," warned Pasteur quite gaily as they left the Ecole Normale, "don't mix up the capsules." Arriving at the station at Melun, they started for Pouilly-le-Fort, and were joined by a crowd of physicians, veterinarians, and farmers who had also come on the train. A few hoped that Pasteur's public demonstration would succeed, but most of those in the crowd rejoiced that at last they had opportunity to attack him out of the laboratory, in the open field. Here at last was an experiment that everyone could follow.

M. Rossignol led Chamberland and Roux to a large shed where fifty sheep were housed. A partition divided them into two lots of twenty-five each. They proceeded to vaccinate all those in lot 1. Those in lot 2 were left untouched. On the sixth, seventh, eighth, and ninth the assistants returned to Melun, examined each of the vaccinated sheep and took their temperature. All twenty-five remained in perfect health.

May 17 was chosen as the day for the second, slightly stronger vaccine, which though weakened, was toxic enough to have caused the death of at least 50 per cent of the sheep had it been given as the first injection. Again, Chamberland and Roux returned every day to observe the vaccinated animals. They still remained in perfect health.

May 31 was selected as the day for the crucial test. Again a large crowd gathered to watch the assistants as they injected all *fifty* sheep with the deadly, living anthrax culture. Two days later the results would be known to all.

Twenty-four hours before this great moment came, the assistants returned to Paris announcing that some of the vaccinated sheep showed a rise in temperature. That night a telegram from Rossignol stated that he feared one of the vaccinated animals was dying. Pasteur broke under the mental strain and completely lost courage. As Roux

expressed it: "His faith faltered as if the experimental
method might betray him." Mme. Pasteur, always confident, tried to encourage him.

"I wish," he said to her, "I could crawl into a dark
corner. This will be the ruin of all my work, and all my
hopes."

Pasteur passed a wretched, sleepless night. At nine
o'clock the next morning another telegram from Melun
announced that eighteen of the unvaccinated sheep had
died and that the seven others were sick and dying. All
vaccinated ones were in good health. The message closed
with the words: "Stupendous success."

Pasteur left at once for Melun and arrived at Pouilly-le-
Fort to be greeted by journalists and farmers, and by delegates from the Agricultural Society of Melun and from
medical and veterinarian societies. Applause and shouts
of acclaim rang out as he stepped from the train. Twenty-
two of the unvaccinated sheep were dead, and two were
scarcely able to take their last breath. All twenty-five vaccinated were in perfect health.

Then and there M. Rossignol placed a drop of blood
from one of the dead sheep and examined it under the
microscope. It was seething with anthrax rods. The
most skeptical joined the applause, and Pasteur was escorted back to the station amid cheers and shouts of "Miracle! Miracle!" Not a person was left to criticize, to
doubt, or to question for the twenty-fifth unvaccinated
sheep had died that night.

It is small wonder that Pasteur's courage failed during
that terrible night when he feared this public demonstra-

tion would fail. The strain under which he had been working for over a year was extreme. Not only had he been working on the anthrax problem, but he had started his studies of rabies. He must discover whether mankind could be protected against this most dreadful of all diseases.

But why did he choose rabies as the first disease for human vaccination? Was it because as a young boy in the Jura mountains he had so feared wild wolves? Was it because children bitten by mad dogs screamed when taken to the blacksmith's shop to have their wounds burned with red-hot irons? Did their cries still haunt him? These were undoubtedly some of the reasons, but in addition he saw that if he could save human beings from this dread disease, his doctrine of vaccination would be established in the most spectacular manner.

Pasteur knew that, before any vaccine treatment for rabies was possible, he must find the causative agent, isolate it in pure culture, and produce the disease in some experimental animal. Only then could he work out how to weaken the microbe. So, at the age of fifty-eight, when the energies of many may be waning, he began his attack on rabies.

First he studied the saliva of mad dogs. With unbounded courage, two of his assistants dragged a mad bulldog from its cage and firmly held it while Pasteur, with even greater courage, bent over the animal, inserted a long glass pipette into its mouth and sucked up the frothing saliva. Careful study revealed only harmless microbes. No causative agent could be seen under the microscope, no causative agent could be cultivated in artificial, lifeless media.

Undaunted by this, Pasteur ordered his assistants to inject saliva from a mad dog into the body of a healthy one. This was repeated many times, but the results were variable. Sometimes the injected animal developed rabies in two weeks, sometimes after several months, and sometimes not at all. These results were too unpredictable to give the precision demanded by the experimental method. Other ways of producing the disease must be discovered.

The behavior of a mad dog made it obvious that the nervous system was involved. Pasteur proceeded to remove the brain and spinal cord of a dog dead of rabies. These dissections were made with the greatest sterility precautions. When this material was injected into the body of healthy dogs, unfortunately the results were as varied as when saliva had been used. Again, some other method of producing the disease must be devised.

"Surely," they reasoned, "if infected nerve tissue is injected directly into the brain of a healthy dog, the results should be more consistent." Usually when a critical experiment was suggested, Pasteur ordered it performed at once. This time there was much delay, for Pasteur dreaded to open the skull of a healthy dog, even though it had been put to sleep with chloroform.

One day Roux took matters into his own hands and performed the operation alone. When Pasteur returned to the laboratory the next day and saw the animal unharmed by the removal of a piece of skull, he was overjoyed, and always felt a special fondness for this dog that helped to relieve him of his scruples of performing such an operation.

Nerve tissue from a mad dog injected directly into the brain of a healthy one gave consistent results: all animals developed rabies in about two weeks. This was tremendous progress. Pasteur had discovered that a microbe too small to be seen with the ordinary microscope must be cultured within living cells. Today we call such particles *viruses*.

In taking this step, Pasteur showed that experimental methods are not a set of rules or recipes that must be literally followed. They are ways of reasoning, ways of proceeding according to definite principles. A scientist must have the ingenuity, the insight, and the imagination to apply those principles to the particular aspects of any given problem. Pasteur had not been literally bound to Koch's postulates, but had followed the principles upon which they are based. He had experimentally produced the disease in test animals without *seeing* the microbe, and without culturing it in artificial, lifeless media.

The conquest of rabies still required further refinements before a vaccination program could be determined. The virulence of the virus must be controlled, and the incubation time (the interval between injection and appearance of the disease) must be shortened. Two weeks was too long to wait for the appearance of the disease when hundreds of experiments must be made.

Pasteur turned to rabbits. When the brain of a healthy rabbit was injected with infected nerve tissue from a rabid dog, the rabbit developed rabies. When injections of nerve tissue from rabid rabbits were made from rabbit to rabbit, the toxicity of the virus was greatly increased. Pasteur discovered from twenty-one such transfers that the virus had become so toxic that rabbits died in six days. He now had a virus of known, measured, maximum toxicity. In other words, further transfers from rabbit to rabbit did not make the microbe any more toxic. He could now work with a virus of known, constant strength, and he called this his "fixed" virus. It was the *virulence,* or toxicity, of the virus which had become fixed.

His next problem was to change this fixed virus into others of *known weakness.* How could he weaken the rabies microbe? The microbe of chicken cholera had been weakened by exposure to oxygen for known lengths of time. Could the virus in spinal cords of dead rabbits be weakened in a similar way? These questions haunted him day and night, and Mme. Pasteur wrote to Marie-Louise and René: "Your father is constantly occupied, speaks to me little, very little, rises at dawn; in a word, continues the life which I began with him thirty-five years ago today."

One day, one of Pasteur's assistants, Adrian Loir, went with him into the incubator room to examine some flasks. Roux was trying to find out how long the fixed virus would live in a rabbit spinal cord. For this purpose, Roux had used a flask with two openings. One was plugged with cotton, and the other was stoppered, and attached to it, hanging inside the flask, was the spinal cord. The assistant said: "At the sight of this flask, Pasteur became so absorbed I did not dare disturb him. . . . After remaining silent and motionless a long time, Pasteur took the flask outside, looked at it, then returned it to its place without saying a word. Once back in the laboratory, he ordered me to obtain a number of similar flasks from the glass blower." The sight of Roux's flasks had given him the idea of keeping the spinal cord in a container with caustic potash to prevent putrefaction, and allowing penetration of oxygen to weaken the virus. The famous portrait painted by Edelfeldt shows Pasteur absorbed in the contemplation of one of these flasks. [See photograph section.]

Thus Pasteur conceived the method of weakening the rabies virus. The spinal cord of a rabbit dried for fourteen days was nontoxic, one dried for thirteen days was slightly less so, and so on, until a cord dried for only one day contained viruses, which though slightly weakened, were the most toxic.

Pasteur was now ready to protect dogs against rabies. He first vaccinated them with a cord dried for fourteen days, and the next day with one dried for thirteen days, and so on until the animal had received a final injection of a cord dried only one day. Having completed the vaccine treatment, the dog was then injected with a culture of living, deadly viruses. The dog remained in perfect health. Vaccination of dogs against rabies had at last been achieved.

If humans were to be protected against rabies, a vaccine program must be given *after* the person had been bitten. Since the incubation time in humans can be long—generally several weeks or longer, Pasteur reasoned that there would be time enough to vaccinate a bitten person *follow-ing* the accident. There should be time enough to stimulate the body to build resistance and prevent the viruses from multiplying and invading the brain. He knew that, once they reached the brain, nothing could save the bitten person. But he must first prove that dogs could be saved after being bitten.

News of Pasteur's work with rabies had traveled abroad. A surgeon in England asked when his method could be applied to man. Pasteur wired: "Operation on man still impossible. No possibility at present of sending weakened virus." The Emperor of Brazil wrote asking when the preventive treatment could be given to man. Pasteur answered that he must first protect dogs *after* they had been bitten, and if successful, he must increase the number of such experiments until he was absolutely certain of his results, but even then he said, "I think my hand will tremble when I go on to Mankind."

In 1885, Pasteur took the final step and protected dogs *after* they had been bitten. Any experimental work in the laboratory always invigorated him, but the mere thought of injecting the rabies virus into a human being— no matter how weakened it might be—caused him the greatest mental anguish. Yet the whole purpose of his work had been to protect mankind against this deadly disease. Seriously he considered that the best way to settle his fear was to begin with himself, first giving himself an injection of the living deadly virus and then submitting to the vaccine treatment. But fate intervened and dictated his procedure on July 6, 1885, when nine-year-old Joseph Meister came limping into his laboratory.

CHAPTER 14

Tributes of Gratitude

BY THE TIME Pasteur was sixty years old, he began to receive formal expressions of gratitude for his scientific
achievements. They came first from farmers and veterinarians, and later from the great men of science throughout Europe.

In the summer of 1883 he was summoned from Arbois
to attend an agricultural exhibit in the nearby town of
Aurillac. During the previous year, over six hundred
thousand sheep and eighty thousand oxen had been vaccinated against anthrax. As a token of gratitude, Pasteur
was given a silver-plated bronze cup decorated with a
group of sheep and a tiny syringe. In making the presen-
tation, the mayor said: "Our town of Aurillac is very small,
and you will not find here the brilliant population which
inhabits the great cities; but you will find minds capable
of understanding the scientific and humanitarian mission
which you have so generously undertaken.... Your
name will be on our lips for a long time."

Pasteur walked about studying the farm products and
implements. He talked with each exhibitor, eager as al-

ways, to learn the slightest practical detail which he might use, because, as he had said: "Nothing should be neglected, and a remark from a rough laborer who does well what he has to do is infinitely precious." As he left the grounds, a peasant came running toward him, waving his large hat and shouting: "Long live Pasteur! You have saved my cattle!"

A few weeks later, on July 14, Pasteur went to Dôle to attend a double ceremony. The citizens of his native town were celebrating Bastille Day, the great French national holiday, which marks the beginning of the French Revolution, on July 14, 1789. They were also to honor Pasteur by unveiling a marble plaque attached to the house where he was born. A statue of Peace commemorating the storming of the Bastille in Paris was first unveiled. Then a procession of townspeople moved on down narrow, stone-paved streets to the little lane called *Rue de Tanneurs*. Standing in front of the old tannery, the mayor opened the ceremony with these words: "M. Pasteur is a benefactor of humanity, one of the great men of France. He will remain for all Dolois, and in particular those who, like him, have risen from the ranks of the people, an object of respect as well as an example to follow. . . . We consider it our duty to perpetuate his name in our town."

The director of fine arts removed the sheet covering the plaque saying: "In the name of the government of the Republic, I salute the inscription which commemorates the fact that in this little house, in this little street, was born on December 27, 1822, he who has become one of the greatest scientists of this century . . . and who has, by his admirable labors, increased the glory of France and deserved well of all humanity."

The citizens of Dôle crowded nearer to hear Pasteur who stood before them—a short, square-built man of sixty with jet-black hair and a beard just turning gray. In a clear, deep voice he responded: "Gentlemen, I am profoundly moved by the honor done me by the town of Dôle. Your sympathy has joined on that memorial plate the two great things which have been the passion and the delight of my life: the love of Science and the cult of the home. . . . Oh, my father and my mother! Oh! my dear departed ones, who lived so humbly in this little house, it is to you that I owe all. Your enthusiasms, my valiant mother, you have instilled into me. If I have always associated the greatness of Science with the greatness of France, it is because I was filled with the feelings with which you inspired me. And you, my dear father, whose life was as hard as your hard trade, you have shown me what patience can accomplish in long efforts. It is to you that I owe tenacity in the daily task. . . . I see you now, after a hard day's work, reading at night, from one of those books of contemporary history, some tale of the battles which reminded you of the glorious time of which you were a witness. While teaching me to read, your care was to teach me the greatness of France. Be blessed, both of you, my dear parents, for what you have been, and let me render unto you the homage paid today to this house."

Pasteur's birthplace at Dôle and the old tannery at Arbois stand today as national shrines to his memory. These museums, preserved much as they were in his time, are visited each year by thousands of people, old and young, professional and lay, who come to see the humble origin of the man now honored by all nations of the world.

When Pasteur had received the grand prize at the exhibition in Paris in 1867, few people in that audience knew of his work on wines, and the ovation extended to him was slight. In 1881, however, his presence at the International Medical Congress meeting in London was a different matter. The great auditorium at St. James Hall was completely filled when Pasteur entered accompanied by Jean-Baptiste and René. An usher, recognizing Pasteur, escorted him to his place on the platform reserved for illustrious delegates. As he approached the front of the auditorium, there came outbursts of applause and shouts of acclaim. Pasteur turned to his son saying: "It is no doubt the Prince of Wales who is arriving. I ought to have come sooner." The president of the Congress, overhearing the remark responded: "But it is you that they are all cheering."

In 1884 Pasteur received an honorary degree from the University of Edinburgh, which was celebrating its three-hundredth anniversary. As names of the candidates were called and each came forward to receive his citation, students in the audience applauded. When Pasteur's name was called, there was silence, for everyone was straining to see him, but as he stepped to the platform, the 5,000 members in that great gathering rose and cheered.

Three months later Pasteur represented France at the International Medical Congress at Copenhagen, where

Jean-Baptiste was then serving as secretary of the French Legation. The meetings were officially opened at the Palace of Industry before an impressive audience. At the close of the ceremony, when Pasteur was presented to the King, the Queen of Denmark and the Queen of Greece broke all imperial etiquette and walked toward Pasteur. This, in the words of a French writer of the time, was a "signal proof of the esteem in which our illustrious countryman is held at the Danish court."

After Pasteur had saved the lives of Joseph Meister and Jean Jupille in 1885, news of the success of the rabies treatment rose above the slandering comments of his enemies. Gradually, hundreds of people bitten by rabid animals came to Pasteur for treatment, and it was soon obvious that a new scientific institute was needed. Committees were formed to raise the necessary funds, and within a year, over two million francs had been subscribed.

In 1888, the construction of the Pasteur Institute in Paris was completed, and on November 14 this great building, which stands today as one of the world's leading institutes for medical research, was inaugurated. Politicians, colleagues, collaborators, friends, and students gathered in the large library of the new institute. M. Carnot, President of the French Republic, was master of ceremony. In the speeches which followed, tribute was paid to Pasteur's teachers who, one by one, had died during the passing years: Biot, Balard, and Dumas. Dr. Grancher, the strongest champion of Pasteur's work on rabies, reviewed his achievements which had revolutionized medicine and surgery. Pasteur's passionate struggles to establish truth, and the days of anxiety which he had borne, were not minimized.

This inauguration celebrated a great triumph—the opening of spacious laboratories where men could work and pursue the cause of science. But Pasteur struck a solemn note, felt by all, when he said: "Alas! mine is the bitter grief that I enter it, a man vanquished by Time, deprived of my masters . . ."

He was too moved to deliver his speech and handed it to Jean-Baptiste to read. In his characteristic dramatic style, Pasteur briefly reviewed the history of French education. Addressing the students and young collaborators he warned: "Keep your early enthusiasm, . . . but let it be regulated by rigorous examinations and tests. Never advance anything which cannot be proved in a simple and decisive fashion. Worship the spirit of criticism. . . . What I am now asking you, and you will ask of your pupils later on, is what is most difficult to an inventor. . . . When you have found an important scientific fact and are feverishly anxious to publish it, . . . constrain yourself for days, weeks, years sometimes, to fight with yourself . . . and only proclaim your discovery after having exhausted all contrary hypotheses. But when after so many efforts, you have at last arrived at certainty, your joy is one of the greatest which can be felt by a human soul. . . ."

The new Institute contained a large and luxurious apartment where Pasteur lived during the last seven years of his life. His own active work in the laboratory was over, but as director of the Institute, he went every morning, dressed in a long black cape and small skull cap, to the rabies clinic. He supervised the preparation of each rabies vaccine, and during clinic hours when patients came for rabies treatment, he was the first to arrive. He knew in advance the name of each patient, comforted the children who were frightened, and gave substantial assistance to the very poor.

Today, the Pasteur Institute is guarded by the ideals of its founder, and each year thousands of visitors are conducted through his apartment, which remains just as he left it. In his bedroom hang the portraits of his father and mother, and the old barrelmaker of Besançon, all of which he painted as a young boy.

By May, 1892, preparations were well underway for a celebration of Pasteur's seventieth birthday. Denmark, Sweden, and Norway were the first to form committees composed of scientists and students of Pasteur. In France, the celebrated engraver, M. Roty, designed a medal. On one side appears Pasteur's head in profile, surmounted by the small skull cap. On the reverse are engraved the words: "To Pasteur on his seventieth birthday. France and Humanity grateful."

On December 27, 1892, foreign delegates from many scientific societies, representatives from all the institutions of learning throughout France and from every large city in Europe filled the platform and auditorium in the new building of the Sorbonne. In the first gallery sat other dignitaries, and the second gallery was overflowing with students from the lycées. As the band of the Republican Guard played a march of triumph, Pasteur walked down the aisle of the auditorium supported by the arm of President Carnot.   Thus opened the famous Pasteur Jubilee.

The Minister of Public Instruction spoke first, reviewing Pasteur's achievements, paying tribute to Mme. Pasteur, "who understood him so well and loved him all the better for it, [and gave him] that comforting encouragement of every hour and each moment, without which so many struggles might have exhausted his ardor, arrested his perseverance, and enervated his genius."

One by one, the most important delegates were called to the platform to bring greetings from the institution which each represented.   Lord Lister, who came in the name of the royal societies of London and Edinburgh, was called.   He rose, advancing to Pasteur with outstretched arms, saying: "You have raised the veil which for centuries had covered infectious diseases; you have discovered their microbic nature."   The two great scientists embraced before the assembly.   The final homage was paid by M. Devise, president of the Students' Association, who said to Pasteur: "You have been very great and very good.   You have given a beautiful example to students."

Pasteur was frail, and his voice too weak to be heard throughout that great auditorium.   Jean-Baptiste read his response: "Monsieur, the President of the Republic, your presence transforms an intimate fête into a great ceremony, and makes a simple birthday of a savant a special date for French science. . . .   Gentlemen, by an ingenious and delicate thought, you seem to make the whole of my life pass before my eyes. . . .   You, my colleagues, have witnessed by what series of deductions it was given to me, a disciple of the scientific method, to reach physiological studies. If I have sometimes disturbed the calm of our Academies by somewhat violent discussions, it was because I was passionately defending truth. . . . And you, delegates from foreign nations, who have come so far to give France a proof of sympathy, you bring me the deepest joy that can be felt by a man whose invincible belief is that Science and Peace will triumph over Ignorance and War. . . ." This great, yet solemn, jubilee closed with shouts resounding through the auditorium; "Long live Pasteur! Long live Pasteur!"

This was Pasteur's last public appearance. He continued to live in his spacious and comfortable apartment at the Pasteur Institute, and only his family and his colleagues at work in the adjoining laboratory rooms knew how frail he was, yet how unimpaired was his intellectual energy. Mme. Pasteur, his constant companion as always, read to him each day, and together they discussed the progress of the work of his pupils. One was in Tunis, another in Brazil, and still others in Constantinople and China.

In the spring of 1895 a tent was put up in the garden of the Pasteur Institute where Pasteur could go of an afternoon to enjoy the blossoming horse-chestnut trees and the coming of summer. Workers of the Institute visited him here, and he never failed to make detailed inquiries of their latest experiments. Thousands of French children were being protected from diphtheria with an antitoxin developed by Roux, and the plague bacillus had been isolated.

His most devoted visitor that spring was Chappuis, who was now honorary president of the Academy at Dijon. Their friendship remained unchanged, and as they reminisced, they philosophized about life as they had done for over fifty years. Pasteur never had time nor inclination to discuss his health, and Chappuis always left him deeply saddened to see his beloved friend so weak in body, yet still so strong in mind.

In June, Pasteur and Mme. Pasteur went to spend the summer in Villeneuve l'Etang just outside of Paris. Here an old castle owned by the government had been given to Pasteur ten years previously so that he might carry on his work with rabies. He had had a modest dwelling made in one of the old stables, and it was here that he and Marie had taken refuge from time to time in his declining years. And it was here that now his strength failed and he quietly died on September 28, 1895, surrounded by his family and a few of his disciples.

The little room in which he died was as modest as was the man. It remains in all its austerity just as he left it. There is a bed, a chair, a table, and on the wall are the markings he made of the growing heights of his grandchildren: Camille Vallery-Radot and Pasteur Vallery-Radot, the latter now a distinguished physician in Paris.

But the French government wished to pay its highest respect to the man who had been so great a benefactor of all mankind, and honored his passing by arranging an impressive national funeral. The cortège, drawn by six horses, was followed by a long line of state dignitaries and Academy members dressed in academic costume. The funeral procession slowly passed from the Pasteur Institute through the streets of Paris, lined on both sides with crowds of reverent, silent citizens, to the Cathedral of Notre Dame. France had lost her favorite son, and the world its greatest scientist of the nineteenth century.

Few great scientists ever live to see the benefits of their work begin to grow and spread as did Louis Pasteur. And no man of greatness ever made contributions which extended into so many fields. The foundations of stereo-chemistry and bacteriology were laid by him, and the methods of industry, agriculture, medicine, surgery, and public health were revolutionized by his discoveries.

Statues of Pasteur perpetuating his memory stand in Paris and in many cities and towns throughout France and Europe. But his immortality lies where he would have it —in the scientific work still developing from the principles he discovered.

Index